WARRIOR

HOW TO SUPPORT THOSE WHO PROTECT US.

STATEMENTS OF SUPPORT

WARRIOR: How to Support Those Who Protect Us

Shauna Springer, Ph.D.

"I stand behind Shauna Springer and her work. She understands the importance of tribe and has valuable insights to share."

Sebastian Junger

Bestselling author of Tribe and War *and Academy Award Winning Filmmaker*

"Shauna Springer, the author of *WARRIOR*, is a warrior in her own right. The insights she delivers are the product of rarely given trust and openness that she's earned over years with our warfighter community. The battle against veteran suicides isn't yet won, but Shauna's presence on that battlefield gives all of us, veterans and those who want to help them, hope for victory."

Karl Marlantes

Bestselling author of Matterhorn *and recipient of the Navy Cross, a Bronze Star, two Navy Commendation Medals for valor, two Purple Hearts, and 10 Air Medals*

"You expose yourself to a Doctor. You reveal yourself to a 'Doc.' 'Doc' Shauna Springer is a civilian psychologist that warfighters embrace as a part of the tribe."

Magnus Johnson

Former Green Beret

"Over 19 years as an infantry Marine and I have never met someone like Shauna 'Doc' Springer. She was able to empathize with me, become a part of the pack, and translate my inner thoughts into constructive interactions. I think of her as one of the corpsmen embedded into my platoon. Nothing but love!"

Keola Lee

First Sergeant, U.S. Marine Corps

"I wish there would have been a book such as *WARRIOR* 51 years ago when I came back from Vietnam after being in the unit that had the highest casualty rates in Marine Corps history the 1stBn, 9th Marines. By reading Doc Springer's book I may not have carried survivor's guilt and self-medicated to numb the pain for so many years. I may not have lost a Marine grandson to suicide if I had been a better role model. This is an outstanding read by an author who, if you didn't know better, would think was a Marine."

Dana O'Brien

Former Sergeant of Marines, 1966-1972

"If you've ever been pinned down in the killzone, you've felt the internal collision of rage, helplessness and frustration. Now remember the feeling that wells up in you on hearing the distinctive sound of attack helicopters inbound. That is Shauna Springer — she is the only civilian psychologist equipped to pull struggling warriors into the light with tenacity and teamwork, not condescension or coddling. Doc Springer is here to do the work, and in *WARRIOR* she gets it done."

Dan Jernigan

Marine Corps Officer

"Doc Springer sticks her hand deep into the dark mire and pulls struggling warriors straight into the sunshine — right where they belong."

Major Scott Huesing
Bestselling author, Echo in Ramadi

"Doc Springer has been there for us since day one. She has been a part of our 'sacred circle.' She has heard and seen our souls' cry."

Rumaldo Parra
Master Sergeant, United States Marine Corps (Ret)

"Dr. Shauna Springer has gained the trust of the very guarded warfighter community and changed the way we look at healing trauma."

Mike Ergo, LCSW
Operation Iraqi Freedom Marine Corps Combat Veteran and Sponsored Ironman Triathlete

"Doc Springer is one of us. She understands a warrior's worth beyond war. I am very skeptical of doctors and psychologists due to past experiences with the VA, but I knew after our first interaction that she was there because she truly cared and that helping us survive is her life's work. She is a key member of my tribe, and I know she's always got our six!"

David Bachmann
Operation Iraqi Freedom Marine Corps Combat Veteran, 2nd battalion, 7th Marines

"Doc, you've been tattooed onto the fabric of this Warrior tribe and we wouldn't be the same without you. Semper Fi."

Brian Vargas, MSW
Operation Iraqi Freedom Marine Corps Combat Veteran, 3/4 Lima Company

"Doc Springer is able to break through to some of the most stoic military groups. She delivers these insights at the tactical, operational and strategic levels with thunder-like precision....On Target! She has demonstrated the ability to manage crucial decision-making points which are only seen from the very best leaders that I have seen in 28 years in the military."

Hector Franco

Sergeant Major, U.S. Army (Ret)

"Doc Springer understands the impact war has on the warfighter, and how these experiences destroy lives. Her wisdom, both penetrating and insightful, has the power to save a life. For anyone struggling to rediscover enjoyment and trust, please read her words, and then pass them on to as many as you can."

Bill Edmonds

Special Forces Officer and author of God Is Not Here

"The SOF community and the Warriors that make it up are a different breed of folks. When Doc Springer began to speak, it was as if she had been inside MY HEAD, as if she were speaking directly to me about me! From that moment she had my undivided attention."

Chris Baird

Hospital Corpsmen, U.S. Navy (Ret)

"Before I met Doc Springer, I was isolated with my personal demons. Doc Springer turned my life around. She led me through a personal catharsis I could not have done alone and got me through to the high ground on the other side. She provided the covering fire so I could confront my demons, realize that I am not alone, and maneuver through my struggle. She is a permanent member of my Tribe."

Rich Stinson

LTC, U.S. Army (Ret)

"If you are in a fight for your own mental wellness or that of your beloved battle buddies (whether military, first responder, medical, humanitarian, etc.) then arm yourself with the best weapon to win. I, personally, witnessed and benefit from Doc Shauna Springer's heart for warriors and life-saving work... We need warriors in our tribe to order, read, and sew deeply down into your heart the lessons of this book; they are written in blood."

NC WEST
Army Veteran and Military Spouse

"Dr. Shauna Springer's *WARRIOR* is exactly what our civilian supporters, employers, military, and veteran community need to truly understand and support our combat veterans. She is the only mental health professional I have met who unequivocally understands the warrior ethos as well as the psychology and healing to guide those struggling through combat trauma. I have been the spouse of an Infantryman for 26 years. After 19 years of combat deployments, we have walked the path with many friends (Soldiers and spouses) who have struggled with combat trauma. *WARRIOR* has opened my eyes to another side of supporting and understanding combat trauma that I never imagined. I highly recommend it to any reader who works with, supports, or loves a combat veteran.

Pay attention to, follow, and support Dr. Shauna Springer's work. She is moving mountains for combat veterans."

Amy Shick
Army Spouse, Military Spouse Entrepreneur

"As a three-time combat veteran and former battalion commander, I salute Dr. Springer's leadership in forging a new path to address the issue of moral injury to help this and future generations of veterans lead healthy, fulfilled lives when they remove the uniform. I don't see her as a practitioner that supports the military community; I see her as standing within our ranks to tackle those unspeakable issues shoulder to shoulder with the men and women who endure invisible wounds from otherwise forgotten wars."

Jason Roncoroni

LTC, U.S. Army (Ret), and bestselling co-author of BEYOND THE MILITARY: A Leader's Handbook for Warrior Reintegration

"Dr. Springer leads the therapist on a journey to uncover the most vital aspects of military culture within the context of the modern operating environment and carefully articulates their relevance to the resolution of psychological trauma. Her intellectual depth emerges throughout the book, empowering clinicians to establish trust and evoke transformative processes with military clients and family members. This is a must-read for any clinician seeking to gain an accurate and in-depth understanding of complex trauma within the military and first responder professions."

Major Josh Mantz

U.S. Army (Ret) and bestselling author of The Beauty of a Darker Soul

"Dr. Springer has embedded her life into the military and veteran community. She understands how and when to ask bold questions and make necessary blunt statements in order to heal or guide veterans' issues. Her book is based on her tireless work and is not a repeat of what we already know."

Nathan Johnson

Contra Costa County Veterans Service Officer and Marine Corps veteran

"Dr. Shauna Springer has proven to be an asset to leadership within both the military and veteran community. Her dedication to veterans and their families is very clear, and she has uniquely perceptive abilities that are greatly valued within the suicide prevention community. A true treasure."

Dr. Keita Franklin
Former National Director of Suicide Prevention for the U.S. Department of Veterans Affairs Office of Mental Health and Suicide Prevention

"Shauna's creative and ingenious approach is a welcome addition to the national dialogue on suicide prevention. She effectively cuts across disciplines and breaks down prohibitive silos to bring through a new way of understanding a complex issue to both military/veteran and civilian populations. The field of suicide prevention and our communities are much better off thanks to Shauna and her work."

Colleen Creighton
Executive Director of the American Association of Suicidology

"Dr. Shauna Springer's new book is expanding our understanding of warriors, society, and how relationships can help them heal. Her work is adding to a growing body of significant research and thinking that is connecting PTSD, suicide, and moral injury. In this book, she is both theoretical and practical, sharing treatment approaches that have really worked for our veterans."

Chaplain Michael L. McCoy, SES, (EQL)
National Director/Chaplain Service, National Chaplain Center, Office of Patient Care Services, Department Veterans Affairs

"I had the pleasure of working with Dr. Shauna Springer while she was a provider at VA Northern California Healthcare System. She was consistently innovative, creative, and brave when tackling veterans' treatment. Her insight and wisdom related to veteran care will be extremely valuable to the veteran community — providers, families and veterans alike."

Brian C. Adkinson, LCSW

Former Suicide Prevention and REACH VET Program Manager, VA Northern California Health Care System (NCHCS)

"I have personally witnessed Dr. Springer's ability to transform combat veterans from the darkest moments in life to being able to function and live normal social and occupational lives. She fully understands the hidden pain of our nations' warriors and how to transform them. A must read for all mental health professionals."

Jeff Jewell

Air Force veteran; former director, Concord Vet Center

"I have experienced Dr. Springer's passion for identifying and understanding how the scars of combat present themselves with our veterans, and how she leverages her compassion and unique cultural sensitivity for those whom she comes in contact with. My company has sponsored her efforts during the past few years across the veteran population, and we look forward to her continued engagement with senior-level behavioral health professionals at my company to socialize her process with a comprehensive 'wellness' training curriculum that incorporates veteran issues and is offered to civilians as well."

Scott Whitacre

Regional co-chair, Kaiser Permanente Veterans Association; Marine Corps veteran

"I have had the privilege of reading an early version of Dr. Shauna Springer's book and heartily recommend it to anyone who is a veteran or who has a friend or family member who is a veteran. Her long-term work with veterans in the VA system has given her real life insight into the psychological pain that many are suffering as a result of their combat experiences. Her strategies for coping with these feelings and developing healthier ways to integrate into 'normality' provide hope for both veterans and their families."

Steven Burchik
Vietnam veteran (U.S. Army); author of Compass and a Camera: A Year in Vietnam

"Perhaps no generation of Warriors has faced more challenges than those who have served our country since 9/11. Many Warriors have served multiple tours, faced increasingly lethal weaponry and come back to a country not prepared to support them. Doc Springer has stepped into a void and continues to provide an amazing service to our Warriors, their families, and to our country."

Michael Gilson
USAF Security Service 1966-1970 and President, Lafayette War Veterans, Inc.

"Doc Springer is a rare and exceptionally gifted healer, a 'warrior whisperer,' who intuitively sees the invisible wounds of the heart, mind, and soul. Her ability to translate suffering into a path to healing and wholeness, so others may walk that path together, is profoundly inspiring and a gift to us all."

Jane Dickerson
President and Founder, Trauma-Sensitive Awareness Foundation

"'Doc' Springer's *WARRIOR: How to Support Those Who Protect Us*, is a seminal work for anyone interested in solutions to the Veteran suicide epidemic. She expertly reinforces a tenet of true experts who treat Veterans that treatment is successful only when trust is first established with the Veteran — when the provider turns from 'Doctor' to 'Doc.' Her most insightful assertion, however, concerns the current widespread practice of building individual resilience. Doc Springer states 'As a society, we continue to make the mistake of thinking that individual outcomes are mainly a product of individual resilience factors.' She goes on to assert, 'Instead of trying to develop individual resilience, we should work to connect people to their tribe, which offers a powerful protective factor.' These assertions call into question the fundamental approach to suicide prevention practiced by the VA and the DoD for the past decade, and the military-civilian transition process as well. And, since the problem of Veteran suicides is relatively worse (compared to the non-Veteran U.S. population) than it was a decade ago, her challenge to current practice is timely and relevant.

Read Doc Springer's book if you want to be challenged and are interested in real solutions to Veteran suicide."

RADM Anthony Kurta

U.S. Navy (Ret) and former Acting Under Secretary of Defense for Personnel and Readiness

WARRIOR

HOW TO SUPPORT THOSE WHO PROTECT US.

SHAUNA SPRINGER, PH.D.

(San Francisco, CA)

WARRIOR: How to Support Those Who Protect Us

Cover Design by Jamie Mustard and Mark Slotemaker

For further information, visit www.docshaunaspringer.com.

Library of Congress Control Number: 2021907717

ISBN: 978-1-7368244-0-5

WARRIOR: How to Support Those Who Protect Us

is available as an audiobook

The audiobook, produced by Tantor Media, was a collaboration between:

Sgt Eddie Wright

(who wrote the foreword)

Major Scott Huesing

(who narrated the foreword) and

Doc Shauna Springer

(who wrote and narrated the content in *WARRIOR*)

To download a copy of the audiobook, visit:
https://tantor.com/warrior-shauna-springer-phd.html

I dedicate this book to Lt. Col. Brett A. Hart, call sign "Stork," a good Marine who is irreplaceable to the many Marines he supported and to those in his home front tribe who deeply love him.

FOREWORD

I opened my eyes. I knew I wasn't dead, not yet, anyway. The world came into view. For a second, I thought the enemy had stopped firing at us. They hadn't. We were all deaf from the RPG blast.[1] It had detonated two feet from my face. My left arm was burning. I looked down and saw what was left of it. It was blown off about midforearm. I could see my jagged, splintered bones jutting out from a bloody, scorched, flayed-open stump. I knew I had lost my left hand.

My right hand was killing me. I raised it up in front of my face to get a good look at it. It was blown off at the base of my hand. There were a few uneven bone fragments sticking out where my palm used to be. It looked as if some of the skin that used to be my hand was dangling, shredded to pieces like someone had removed all the bone and flesh from inside. It hung like an empty glove that had gone a few rounds with a garbage disposal. I thought, "Fuck, *both* of them!"

I wasn't done assessing the situation, though. I looked down and saw that my left leg was blown wide open, my femur split in half like a jagged, splintered water hose. It pumped out huge amounts of blood with every heartbeat. Imagine a coffee cup full of blood, hot blood. Now imagine that every time your heart beats, you toss about that much blood out of your cup and down your thigh. The coffee cup would fill up again in between heartbeats. I knew I only had so many cups of coffee left in me.

My leg had almost been blown in half. I took one look at the gleaming white bone sticking out of a sea of red, and I knew I was dead if I didn't stop that bleeding. How was I going to get a tourniquet on my leg and both arms when I didn't have hands? The fight wasn't over yet. I knew I needed to use my head.

Trauma sucks. Even for combat veterans. I don't think anyone would disagree. I do, however, think combat veterans have unique resiliency and fortitude to deal with trauma. Somewhere along the line, I feel America's perspective changed towards combat-wounded veterans and the trauma we experienced. Where once we were venerated, now we are often pitied. I speak from personal experience. I was no stranger to war on the day that I lost my arms and nearly bled to death, in Fallujah, Iraq. I was injured during my second deployment to Iraq, having taken part in the invasion in 2003 prior to that. There wasn't much I hadn't seen or experienced by then.

I remember waking up in the Intensive Care Unit (ICU) at the National Naval Medical Center (NNMC) Bethesda Maryland Hospital. I think the ICU staff thought I had sustained a serious head trauma because of my attitude. I was happy. Too happy. It didn't make sense to them, and I don't blame them for being confused. Hell, I used to tell my teammates that if I ever lost an arm or a leg, they should go ahead and put me out of my misery.

From the outside looking in, I should have been devastated. Both my hands were blown off completely. My left leg was wrapped in plastic, the tissue of my thigh and shin shredded to oblivion. Skin grafts were in the near future for me. No less than six suction tubes connected me to the wall. I could see my injuries, and I could remember every bit of the sights, sounds, and pain associated with taking a direct hit with an RPG. What a horrible thing for anyone to have to go through. Right? Yes, perhaps, if you allow yourself that perspective. But that's not my perspective, and perspective is the hallmark of resilience.

The first time I met Doc Springer face-to-face was in Chicago. I was there to undergo a medical procedure called stellate ganglion block, a promising new treatment for symptoms of trauma. It had been fourteen years since I was wounded … fourteen years that weren't easy. Recently, I had decided to man up and be the warrior I know I am. To me, this meant I had to finally work on my mental fitness with as much, if not more, effort than I had put into my physical fitness or any other discipline.

I am fortunate that in my journey towards improving my mindset and emotional well-being, a brother I served with introduced me to Doc Springer. I had seen firsthand how her approach had helped out my fellow combat veteran so much. That was enough for me personally to "vet" her, as we veterans like to do. Before I was wheeled back to the procedure room, I had a conversation with Doc Springer, who was bedside before, during, and after the procedure, providing overwatch like she does.

As I progressed through the procedure, we spoke about personal concerns of mine and of trauma. I explained to Doc Springer that what I struggled with daily was not the loss of my hands or the disability it implied. She nodded with a look of recognition and said to me, "I bet a lot of people assume that your biggest trauma, the one that has been the most challenging, is the loss of your arms, but I can see that that's not the case for you. You've adapted and overcome in that area the way that Marines do. Your trauma is not what most people assume." And this is the truth that many people — even people with advanced clinical training — cannot see.

What I struggled with was the trauma I had experienced throughout my entire life, not just my combat experience — least of all my combat wounds. By the time I got injured in Iraq, my trauma was already in place. And any trauma I sustained on the day I got hit by the RPG was far overshadowed by the pride I felt.

As I explained to Doc Springer, in becoming a Recon Marine, I felt like I had accomplished my greatest goal. I was part of an elite team of warriors. On that day in Iraq, despite life-threatening injuries, I acquitted myself honorably on the battlefield. I lost my hands as a true warrior.

For myself, and so many other veterans, the term "hero" makes us feel awkward. What feels more awkward, though, is to hear that term book-ended in a conversation by pity.

Doc Springer doesn't emit pity because she understands the warrior spirit at an instinctive level. She has a no-nonsense approach to treating or preventing PTS. She communicates that we are strong enough to overcome the challenges before us and that we can do this by using skills we possess already, whether we realize it or not.

This is a book about the challenges we face, but make no mistake about Doc Springer's approach. She doesn't see us as broken. She calls to our strength and she walks with us in a way that translates like this: I see the challenges before you, and I can help you get clear on them as well. Now, get up and fight.

Sergeant Eddie Wright

U.S. Marine Corps (Ret), Bravo Co. 2nd Plt. 1st Reconnaissance Bn., OIF I, II

PREFACE

Every year, we donate hundreds of millions of dollars to causes that support service members, veterans, and first responders. We allow our military service members to board airplanes before we do. We honor them at ballgames. We have an insatiable appetite for movies like *American Sniper*, books written by Navy SEALs, and warrior stories on television like *Jack Ryan*, *The Unit*, and *SEAL Team*. The preview for the remake of *Top Gun* instantly went viral. All of this suggests that we are interested in the experiences of our nation's warriors, and we care about the well-being of those who risk it all to protect us.

And yet, despite all the thanking veterans for their service, *today's veterans tell me that they feel no better understood by society than our Vietnam veterans did*. They tell me that they often feel invisible, like ghosts trying to navigate through a culture that has values that are completely different than their values.

Many people in society — including a fairly large number of therapists — seem to think that veterans come back traumatized by what they see and do in combat. Through public and private funding, we have invested hundreds of millions of dollars to develop effective treatments for post-traumatic stress, and to diagnose and better understand TBI. We are told that these are the "invisible wounds of war." We have trained up thousands of clinicians across the VA to deliver empirically supported treatments for the "trauma of being exposed to war."

And yet, the idea that veterans die by suicide because they deploy to war zones is a misconception: A 2015 study of nearly four million U.S. service members and veterans found that deployment to Iraq and Afghanistan is not associated with an increased risk of suicide.[2] There are some injuries that are even more invisible, more insidious, and more lethal than the "invisible wounds of war" that we have focused so much time and money to address. For many of my patients, the hidden pain they carried came from other sources. For instance, five very common sources were childhood traumas; moral injuries; past experiences of social rejection upon entering treatment settings; feelings of alienation from their closest family members and civilians in general; and the helpless rage and overwhelming grief of losing fellow veterans to combat, training accidents, and suicide.

How Can Warriors Be "Heroes" and "Broken" at the Same Time?

My most recent book, *BEYOND THE MILITARY: A Leader's Handbook for Warrior Reintegration*, was written to shift the paradigm of transition. Instead of seeing veterans as "broken" and needing help to go from a sitting position to a standing position, *BEYOND THE MILITARY* provides a roadmap to help warriors fulfill their full potential in life after military service.

Our nation's warriors have an abundance of grit, but they are not superhuman. They are humans — just like us — with a clarity of purpose, and bonds of love and trust, that allow them to accomplish superhuman feats. This is a book about the challenges faced by some of our strongest and bravest citizens. It is necessary to focus targeted attention on these challenges if we are to better understand them. But as Sgt. Eddie Wright expressed in the foreword, this is not a book that perpetuates the myth that warriors are "broken."

Armed with the right insights, warriors can and will heal and go on to become stronger than they have ever been. Traumas don't just break us down; they are defining moments that can show us how strong we really are. They are moments that help us see our deeper purpose and the values that guide a meaningful life.

And strength takes on different forms in different contexts. In battle, it might mean suppressing our natural human emotions in the heat of a firefight to stay laser focused on our objective. In mental warfare, it might mean taking the harder path — acknowledging our struggles with those we trust and drawing from the strength of our tribe to overcome these struggles.

Who Is a Healer, Really?

A doctor, with many years of formal education and training, may or may not be a healer. In some cases, the way a doctor practices is the reason why a veteran drops out of treatment, never to return. But a "Doc," someone who builds the kind of deep trust veterans had in the service with their medics — that person is a healer.

A wife or a parent who recognizes and helps carry the grief of their military loved one — these are healers.

A husband who listens with love and empathy to his warrior wife — he becomes essential in bringing her *all the way home*.

Fellow students in classrooms who respectfully integrate veterans into their college communities — they become healers.

Even actors who turn down roles that perpetuate one-dimensional myths of veterans as either heroes or broken gear, who instead pursue roles that portray veterans as multifaceted human beings (like all of us) — they become healers.

What is a healer? It is all of us, or none of us, depending on what we understand and how this moves us to act in support of those who protect us.

The Surprise Gift

We can learn much about our own condition by understanding those who protect us — their struggles, their triumphs, their bonds with each other. In the vein of Sebastian Junger's *Tribe*, there are indescribably beautiful aspects to the connection that military brothers and sisters share. Like Junger's *Tribe*, *WARRIOR* is a true crossover, knitting together the worlds of the warrior and those they protect in thought-provoking ways.

Additionally, rather than applying solely to those who serve in the military, and those who care for them, *WARRIOR* seeks to develop psychological insight and meaningful personal growth for a broad readership through close observation of how hidden pain, courage, and love show up in the stories of some of the bravest men and women in our society.

WARRIOR gives thoughtful consideration to subjects that have not been well explored as yet, for example, moral injury; how to approach conversations about firearm safety; the links between shame, grief, and suicidal ideation; the ways that current suicide prevention approaches may be failing us; the trust gap between warriors and civilian treatment providers, and the bond between veterans and their trusted healers. The subjects in the book are not only undeveloped as yet, but they are also critical and very timely. Finally, a unique feature of the book is that insights are paired with exercises and questions for further reflection.

Writing this book has been a labor of love. I have walked on sacred ground with many of our nation's service members, veterans, and first responders. As we have walked together, I have learned a great deal from them. They have taught me about different kinds of courage and bonds of love with a power greater than despair. I hope that what I've written here helps us to better support those who risk it all to protect us, and to better support each other as well.

TABLE OF CONTENTS

Foreword xxi

Preface xxv

Introduction 1

Chapter 1. A Little Secret About Secrets 5

Chapter 2. What Is Strength, Really? 21

Chapter 3. The Myth of the Broken Ones 35

Chapter 4. A Loaded Conversation 49

Chapter 5. Shame on You 65

Chapter 6. Foxes 89

Chapter 7. A Warrior Without Armor 107

Chapter 8. Friendly Fire 125

Chapter 9. Our Greatest Power 147

Chapter 10. A Different Kind of War 163

Afterword 185

Epilogue 189

A Mental Healthcare Manifesto 211

Acknowledgments 217

Handbook of Worksheets and Exercises 221

Emotional Safety Self-Assessment 223

Exercise: Sharing with Providers (for patients) 241

Exercise: Owning Your Recovery Journey (for patients) 243

Exercise: Reconnecting with a Fallen Battle Buddy 245

Recommended Reading List 247

Glossary of Terms and Phrases that We May Need to Rethink 251

The Warrior Box Project 259

Endnotes 261

Preview of *Beyond the Military* 273

Preview of Doc Springer's Next Book with Michael Sugrue 277

About the Author 283

INTRODUCTION

The story goes that a boy of Sparta stole a fox and concealed it under his cloak. As he was sitting in the classroom, surrounded by other students and instructors, the fox began to eat his midsection. The boy sat without moving — in plain view of lots of people — while the fox continued to hollow out his stomach, until finally, without a cry of pain, he suddenly dropped dead. The legend of the boy of Sparta has been used to illustrate the value the Spartan culture placed on stoicism, in other words, suffering in silence.

I think the legend of the boy of Sparta is actually about shame. In fact, in *Gates of Fire*, a depiction of the Spartans and the epic Battle of Thermopylae, author Steven Pressfield artfully alludes to the proverbial fox when speaking of "the secret shame of the warrior: the knowledge within his own heart that he could have done better, done more, done it more swiftly or with less self-preserving hesitation; this censure … gnawed unspoken and unrelieved at the men's guts."[3]

Hidden pain is like a fox in our gut. It can silently, steadily hollow us out over time. Suffering in silence can be dangerous, even lethal in some cases. Guilt, shame, and private burdens of grief may become deadly enemies for some of the strongest, bravest people in our society — our combat warfighters. However, let me be very clear: Although the insights shared in this book came from my frontline work with hundreds of veterans, these are not "veterans' issues." These are human issues. The way we handle our hidden pain as individuals and as a society will determine our growth and renewal, or our collective decay.

By examining the greatest vulnerabilities of our strongest and bravest citizens, we can gain new insight into things that many of us thought we understood: for example, trust, stigma, firearms, the imploding mind, and connection. As well as offering us a window into how our bravest citizens may struggle, our warfighters have much to teach us about true courage and the bonds of love that keep us in the fight. The chapters to follow focus on themes of hidden pain, courage, and love, viewed through the lens of my work with veterans, with many areas of wide-ranging application to help all of us deepen our relationships and live better lives.

Each chapter traces a stream of observations from my work with veterans into an array of insights about the human condition. Chapters 1 through 4 draw back the curtain on the scene of where veterans receive their care, showing us how a cultural and trust gap between veterans and many of the healers that hope to support them becomes a barrier to care.

Chapter 1 examines the cultural divide between frontline emotional responders to veterans and first responders — those who work in mental health clinics. We explore the importance of developing trust if we are ever to see the hidden pain of those we serve. We also reflect on how the very things that we often use to establish trust can actually work against building trust with those we are trying to reach.

Chapter 2 takes a fresh look at stigma to help us see why some people who are new to care are actively looking for a good reason to never return. We explore what it takes to overcome stigma and how progressing in treatment calls for a new definition of strength.

Chapter 3 examines the myths we create and the stories we tell that are shaming to groups of people. We examine how this shame plays out, even in the spaces that are set up to be the "safest" and most supportive healing environments we have to offer.

Chapter 4 explores how physical objects and tools can become extensions of our identity, as in the case of firearms for many of our combat warfighters and first responders. We examine why conversations about firearm safety are so challenging and why they may lead those we serve to drop out of care entirely. We also explore several ways to change the conversation, so that we can better align ourselves with those we are serving.

Chapters 5 and 6 examine the hidden pain that is often more invisible than the "invisible wounds of war" — moral injury, guilt, shame, and grief. Chapter 5 illustrates how guilt and shame can become lethal. We explore the story of suicide and how shame may be the critical, overlooked link in the explanatory model for many who die by suicide, both veterans and civilians alike.

Chapter 6 focuses on how the bonds of love we share can be both life threatening and life renewing. We explore human connection, in the context of grief and loss, and we reflect on how we can carry love forward to create a meaningful life.

Chapter 7 explores a different type of courage than the courage required to meet a flesh-and-blood enemy in the combat zone. We examine the kind of courage that allows us to be vulnerable with those we love and trust. We also reflect on how the ability to extend one's tribe beyond just one group of individuals is critical for our long-term health and happiness.

Chapter 8 takes a fresh look at conflict in our closest relationships. We explore the value of conflict and develop key insights for learning to have a good fight.

Chapters 9 and 10 provide a fresh perspective that will help us get traction in a different kind of war — the one that can happen in our minds. Chapter 9 suggests that our current suicide prevention strategies have not been based on the right questions or the best possible approach. We observe that there is a power greater than despair, and we take a close look at what keeps us in the fight during our times of greatest struggle.

Finally, in Chapter 10, I argue that without a clear understanding of the challenge at hand, we cannot build a good strategy for action. I provide a tactical analysis of how despair comes over us and what we can do to overcome this despair. Chapter 10 also contains specific examples of innovative suicide prevention approaches that have come from many years of frontline work with those who have found hope within the deepest valleys of their lives.

1

A LITTLE SECRET ABOUT SECRETS

About ten years ago, I accepted a job at the Department of Veterans Affairs (VA), hoping to make a difference in the lives of our nation's veterans. Taking a job at the VA was my way of serving our country. I wanted to deploy the training I had received over many years in graduate school to benefit my veteran patients. I was idealistic and brimming with optimism.[4]

On my first day at the VA, my new supervisor handed me a list of approximately 100 names and said, "These vets have been waiting for you to start for the past several months.[5] Call all of them, find out what they need, and get them scheduled if they want to come in. Fair warning: a good number of them are mad about how long it took us to get you hired and on-boarded in place of the last psychologist, who was well liked by his patients." I hadn't even met my patients and I was already in the hole.

Most of the people I called were gracious, but as I had been warned, some of them were very angry. On hearing my voice, one patient said, "So you're the new hire? What are you — like twenty-five years old? Why do they keep hiring people who can't relate to veterans, who have no military or life experience?!" I flushed hot with shame, stung by the intensity of his criticism.

On some level, I knew this wasn't about me, but on another level, he had a point. Who was I to presume that I could understand the experiences of combat warfighters when I had spent the better part of the last decade in graduate school? This is the thought that shamed me, that I had nothing of value to offer to those I wanted to support.

Based on these initial outreach calls to my new patients, it became obvious that there was a deep cultural gap — and a trust gap — that would need to be overcome if I were to be useful in my new role. At the time, it was hard to come into such a hostile environment in the first weeks of my new job. In retrospect, though, it was a gift and an opportunity for growth in disguise, as many growth opportunities are. The initial anger I felt from some of my patients, which I knew on some level was not personal, nonetheless compelled me to take a hard look at how to build trust with all of them.

I decided to approach my time at the VA like an enlistment. I would serve four years and then decide whether or not to "reenlist" for another four years. I spent the next eight years (to the day) examining any barriers to trust that I could control. I thought about who my patients perceived me to be, as a relatively young, blonde civilian female, in the early part of my career. I considered the way I decorated my office space, even the way I dressed.[6]

Most important, I realized that in replacing a provider they trusted, I was the "FNG" (the "f-cking new guy") from where my patients sat. They had attached to him and had trusted him with their private pain. In replacing him, I had to overcome both a deficit of trust and the residual effects of an unexpectedly severed attachment with their previous doc.

Trust Outranks Rank

Many of this initial group of patients were Vietnam veterans, and so for many of them, there was a further, deeper dimension to the initial gap in trust between us. Understanding leadership structures in the military is the key for gaining insight. For those who are unfamiliar with military culture, there are often two parallel lines of leadership in military rank structures. Some leaders are noncommissioned officers (NCOs) who rise from within, gaining credibility from their boots-on-the-ground experience. Others gain rank by attending colleges or military institutions and enter leadership roles as commissioned officers.

Many of those who were drafted into the Vietnam War or who enlisted grew to distrust commissioned officers tasked with leading units and developing combat strategies. During the Vietnam War, it was not uncommon for an officer with no prior combat zone experience to be appointed to a leadership position that would outrank someone with significant time "in country." In any case, decisions made in combat scenarios have very high stakes. It is therefore adaptive for those already in the field to regard newly assigned officers as a potential liability, until proven otherwise.

Newly minted officers without prior boots-on-the-ground experience are often out of touch with the combat tactics that are most effective within a given theater of conflict. Of course, this is no fault of their own. How would one know the best approach to take without direct knowledge of the combat theater? In such scenarios, the best officers — the ones their soldiers or Marines would take a bullet for — accepted guidance from their experienced NCOs. The proud and foolish among them were a liability to their soldiers, perhaps issuing authoritarian commands based on limited knowledge and putting their soldiers in reckless engagements as a result.

When I viewed myself through the eyes of these patients, I saw that I would probably be perceived as an "officer" rather than an NCO. The parallel was too close to ignore. I entered the clinical collaboration with a set of higher degrees and lack of direct military service history. Plus, I was early in my career, whereas my predecessor had been relatively more seasoned.

While tension between officers and enlisted was salient for many of my Vietnam veteran patients, this is not nearly as often the case for veterans of more recent wars. However, even if the tension between parallel lines of military leadership has now lessened, any new member of a unit, whether officer or enlisted, is still the "FNG" and thus enters the relationship with a deficit of trust.

In order to earn trust, they must prove that they are effective in their position, which takes time and the right approach. The "rank" of my degree and my time in graduate school paled in importance to the trust I earned with my patients. Over time, I became "Doc Springer" to several hundred veteran patients because I understood that trust must be earned, rather than presumed.

Narrow Window, High Stakes

Ideally, in the places where veterans receive mental health care, clinicians would readily engage the trust of their patients. In a perfect world, the civilian-military cultural divide would be easily traversed in the safe and sacred spaces where an army of providers support our nation's warfighters.

In fact, though, there is a culture and trust gap that becomes a substantial barrier to care for many veterans. I write with urgency. Fourteen of twenty veterans who die by suicide every day are not engaged in VA care.[7] Bridging the divide between civilian providers and those they serve is challenging, and failure can carry life or death consequences.

Professional healers have a very brief window of opportunity to engage our veterans and first responders. The way we approach initial therapy encounters is critical; 70% of all people who drop out of mental health treatment (veterans and civilians alike) do so after their first or second visit.[8] Clinicians and peer support specialists who work with veterans in a rapidly expanding variety of treatment settings are our society's frontline emotional responders for service members as they make the transition to civilian lives.

It is critical for us to build the same trust with the first responders who protect us here at home. We have to figure this out. The lives of many of our warfighters and first responders depends on it.

Two Types of Providers: Doctors and Docs

As I started to see things from the perspective of my patients, and to transform my approach to practice accordingly, I realized that, broadly speaking, there are two types of providers who work with veterans — "doctors" and "docs." A "doctor" is a person with a higher degree and expertise that is recognized in the academic community. This is the default term used for providers with advanced degrees in systems where veterans and first responders receive treatment.

However, calling a provider "Doc" often connotes a special kind of trust. The heart of this distinction lies in the role the provider assumes with his or her patients. As a highly trained Special Forces medic once explained to me when he conferred the name of "Doc" on me, "Doc" is what soldiers call a trusted medic in their combat unit. He said there were three sources of medical care in the Special Forces: licensed MDs (referred to as "Sir"), medics who were unproven (called "medics"), and finally, the ones who could treat and heal other soldiers (called "Doc") because "help was guaranteed when it was needed most." So, I first learned from this precious patient, a man whom I respect and would in turn trust with my life, that a "doc" is a person you can trust with your life. For many veterans, this is the meaning of "doc."

Warriors (service members, veterans, and first responders) have an exquisitely sensitive radar for figuring out where a given provider lands. Docs earn their trust and doctors disproportionately fail to engage them in care. This critical distinction organized my approach to serving our nation's warriors — rather than approaching them as a doctor, I wanted to engage my patients as someone with the same heart as the medics they came to trust in the military. In fact, I now feel that the best compliment

I can receive is when a warrior starts calling me "Doc." To clearly illustrate this distinction, I've created profiles to highlight the key differences between doctors and docs:

1. ***Doctors assume that their patients should trust them based on their many years in school.***

   Based on their training, they are confident they can help. Doctors are the identified "experts" who offer "treatments" to their patients. They generally do not engage with their patients outside of the doctor-patient role. Over time, because they only see their patients in the "patient" role, doctors may develop a cynical, privately negative view of those they serve as "impaired," which can spill over and show up in how they interact with their patients in the clinical setting. The core belief of a doctor is this: *Working with warriors is my job. I use my education and training to offer treatment to help them recover.*

2. ***A doc sees working with warriors as their way to serve those who serve us all.***

   Docs are mission driven, and they want to earn their patients' trust by listening and learning. They typically see veterans as fundamentally resourceful and will often engage them outside of the narrow "patient-provider" role. Instead of engaging warriors in a "one-up, one-down" treatment relationship, docs collaborate with them. Their understanding of the needs of their patients and the culture of service grows over time. The core belief of a doc is this: *Working with warriors is my calling. I want to get better and better at this over time.*

   You can sometimes identify a doctor by a quick visual of their office and an observation of how they conduct their sessions. For example, in their offices, in addition to prominently displaying a collection of advanced degrees, doctors may have "their" chair, which looks different from the chair of a veteran patient. And sometimes, the designated patient chair is thoughtlessly placed in a way that will make a patient feel most vulnerable, with his or her back to the door.

Doctors often direct the care of their patients and give explanations in language that is typical of the medical or psychological field, which may not land with veterans and first responders. For example, you might be in the presence of a doctor if you hear him or her explain something as follows:

> Epictetus discovered that it is not what happens to us, but how we think about the things that have happened that causes depression. Negative cognitions result in cyclical maladaptive patterns of behavior. Over time, we develop cognitive schemas that become rigid, and need to be analyzed and challenged. Here is a thought-restructuring sheet that you can use to challenge your thoughts. In column A, you write down your automatic cognitions, and in column B, you write the automatic beliefs that go with each cognition.

In contrast, a doc might appreciate that there are at least six words here that would make most patients' eyes glaze over, veteran and civilian alike: Epictetus, cognitions, cyclical, maladaptive, schema, analyzed. If we use abstract, ivory tower words like these, we are much less likely to engage our patients. In contrast, a doc might say something like:

> Do you ever feel like you are stuck in a loop, like no matter what you do, you can't get the result you want? Or do you feel repeatedly sucked into the same types of frustrating interactions with your partner or your coworkers? You might even feel repeatedly ambushed by panic attacks or driven to hurt those you love the most by attacks of rage. We all have a "mental map" that helps us figure out how to navigate our relationships.

Taking a closer look at our patterns can help us to update our map and better navigate our way forward. In all likelihood, you already have the skills you need. It's just a matter of connecting with how to use them in a different way. For example, even though your rage makes you feel out of control, remember that when you learned to fire your weapon, you learned to snap in, and to get really calm by controlling your breathing and gently squeezing the trigger between breaths. So, you have the ability to downregulate your body, and because of that, we can work on linking that ability to other challenges in your life.

The issue isn't necessarily the type of therapy someone offers. A doc might also work from a cognitive behavioral therapy approach but would modify his or her language so that it would land with a veteran. Like combat medics, docs have useful skills, and they deploy these skills in ways that connect with the language and culture of military veterans and first responders. As trust grows, a doc becomes an extension of the tribe of those they serve over time (definitely not the tribal chief, but a trusted advisor).

The concept of doctors and docs relates to a podcast I heard on the work of Harvard Business School professor Francesca Gino.[9] During the *Hidden Brain* podcast episode entitled "Rebel with a Cause," Gino describes the hidden cost of expertise. She explains that she and her colleagues became "fascinated by this idea that experience could be costly because in a lot of our classes, they are actually telling our students that they should gain knowledge, that information is power, that experience is important." They explored millions of data points that showed how experienced cardiologists behaved after the FDA announced that the way they were using certain technology was not good for their patients.

What Gino and her colleagues discovered is that the more experience the surgeon had, the less likely they were to change their behavior. She concluded that as we gain experience, we often feel like the expert and we think that we know better, even when valid information sources tell us that we need to rethink our approach. This is the hidden cost of expertise: if we think we know the best way to approach our work, based on our many years in school, we may miss opportunities to see where we need to change our approach, sometimes radically.

Perceptions of Those Who Serve Veterans in the VA System

Sometimes, within the veteran community, there can be negative perceptions of those who work in VA treatment facilities. During my time at the VA, however, I worked with a number of outstanding colleagues. There are many within the VA, like myself, who pursue this work because it is a calling. Many of my fellow clinicians were top notch. The two clinic managers that served during the majority of my time at the VA were both dedicated to offering veterans the highest possible quality of care.

During my time with the Department of Veterans Affairs, I helped launch several innovative programs with the support of my clinic managers. For example, I was the first supervisor and mentor for the peer support specialist program in my clinic. The peer support specialist's role was to use his lived experience of growth in treatment to support the recovery of other veterans. He and I developed strong trust and mutual respect.

Trust is the most important currency you can earn as a healer. As a general rule, trust must be earned with each new patient who presents to therapy. There is an exception to this rule, however: If you are fortunate enough to have a skilled peer support specialist in your clinic, you do not have to build trust from scratch with each new patient.

The peer support specialist and I worked together, as a team, to engage new patients in treatment. He had special abilities to connect that I did not have (or at least, skills I could not have deployed at the speed he was able to deploy them, as a fellow veteran). For his part, he knew that I had his back and he trusted my clinical expertise in a variety of situations that arose during the time we worked together. So, we were able to deploy something I call the "principle of transfer of trust." Here is an illustration of the principle of transfer of trust.

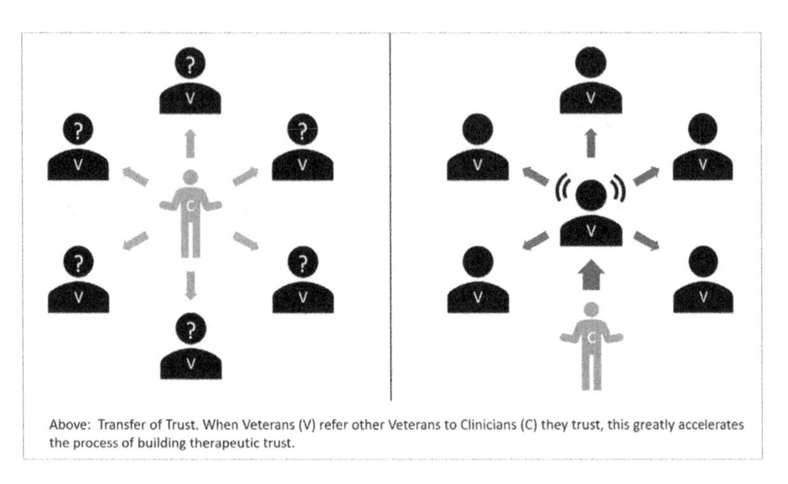

Above: Transfer of Trust. When Veterans (V) refer other Veterans to Clinicians (C) they trust, this greatly accelerates the process of building therapeutic trust.

As shown in this figure, one can gain immediate trust and make quantum leaps in therapy with veterans when a veteran peer bridges the trust. In fact, the peer and I saw a need to better orient new patients, so we launched a new patient briefing group, years before orientation groups became a VA Health Care System requirement. We wanted to help new patients see the potential benefits of behavioral health treatment and give them a working model for how to navigate the system of care. We wanted to give them functional informed consent as early in the process as possible. Our goal was to be the first point of contact with every new veteran who entered the clinic.

During new patient briefing groups, we strategically put our working trust on display. We wanted new patients to immediately witness a healthy, functional relationship between a provider and a peer support specialist. We felt this would go a long way to bridging the gap of trust that is so often a barrier to care. For patients we saw jointly, the principle of transfer of trust was a powerful asset. As a veteran peer, he was able to quickly establish trust with new patients. All it took from that point was for him to say something like, "Doc gets it. She can help you with this." A statement that took him five seconds to say saved me months of sessions building trust with some veterans.

The trust was transferred, even when new patients saw providers other than myself. Because we gave new patients a clear model for what right looks like, our colleagues had an advantage in building trust. Working as a team saved time, helped us deploy our skills much more quickly, and ultimately helped our patients experience relief from their suffering much sooner than they would have otherwise. This programming was supported by our leadership, who shared our vision of offering the highest quality of care to veterans.

Some Wounds Are Even More Invisible than the "Invisible Wounds of War"

The concept of "invisible wounds of war" is important; it brings much-needed credibility and focus to the real pain that affects some of our warfighters and first responders. Unfortunately, it has also become synonymous with post-traumatic stress and traumatic brain injury to the exclusion of other, even more invisible wounds of war.

Treatment is only as good as the truths it is based on. For therapists, it is literally part of our job description to get the full story, but unless we build trust and become docs, we may never hear about the true nature of our patients' pain. We collect information about what we assess — the same story that we read about in the news — the one about post-traumatic stress and blast injuries. As I became their doc, I learned that for many of my patients, the fox in their gut, the one that was eating them alive, was something entirely different. Without trust, these secrets would have remained secret.

UNIVERSAL PRINCIPLES I LEARNED FROM WORKING WITH WARRIORS

1. ***Trust is the most valuable currency we can earn in our relationships.***

   Troops who are ready for battle have the necessary skills to fight, but equally, or perhaps even more important, they have a bond of trust that makes them willing to risk their lives to protect each other. Trust is the lifeblood of effective combat, effective therapy, and authentic relationships.

   Trust defines who is in, and who is outside of one's tribe. Trust is the defining issue in treatment settings for veterans, first responders, and civilians alike. It forms the basis for nearly every mental health treatment relationship, and without it, secrets stay secret. Likewise, the quality and level of intimacy in our close personal relationships is limited to the degree that we can build and maintain trust.

2. ***External credentials don't necessarily translate into trust.***

   We should never presume that others trust us based on external credentials. There are many leaders in society with education, expertise, and sometimes even great vision. While education and prior expertise might be important, they may blind us to what we do not know and limit us from seeing things we really need to see. Often, we need to intentionally put aside what we think we know, and just listen deeply and with curiosity. Ultimately, we cannot be true influencers if we are unable to develop trust with those in our circles because, without trust, we are unlikely to get the full story.

3. ***Developing trust is about doing what we say we're going to do.***

   Trust is in large part a function of the alignment between what we say and what we do. It takes time for trust to grow because others need to see whether we do what we say we're going to do consistently over time. This is particularly true for individuals who have had trauma, multiple severed attachments, or ruptures in trust in the past. Trust and dependability are very closely linked. Dependability communicates respect and a sense of safety. It shows others that they can rely on us. Trust also forms when we handle other people's vulnerability in respectful, steady ways.

4. ***"Fake it till you make it" is terrible advice.***

   Sometimes, we are given the advice to "fake it till you make it." Veterans and other groups of people who have been sensitized to trustworthiness have an exceedingly well-developed bullsh-t detector. If you don't know something, never fake it; they are likely to pick up on it and read the dishonesty in your approach. If we want to connect with someone who has very different life experiences from our own, it's best to be both culturally *curious* and culturally *humble.* Staying open, asking the right questions, and never, ever faking what we don't know is the way to build trust. This is true in other situations and relationships as well. It destroys trust when we put on a false front. Authenticity is always the better path.

QUESTIONS FOR REFLECTION AND APPLICATION

1. In systems of care that support veterans, there are many mission-driven healers (docs) for whom their work is a calling. There are also a number of providers (doctors) who approach their work as the identified experts who offer "treatments" to their patients. How does the distinction of doctors and docs fit with your own experiences of care you have received from your past and current health-care providers?

2. When people in healing roles behave more like doctors than docs, to what degree are they doing this consciously? Is it possible that this behavior may simply be a result of how civilian health-care providers are socialized (i.e., that a formal degree translates into immediate credibility, or the use of terms like "cognitions" and "schemas" that are taught in graduate programs)?

3. How can the concept of developing the kind of trust veterans have with their medics help you make improvements in your own personal and professional relationships? If you were to describe this kind of trust in your own words, how would you explain it?

4. In recent years, cultural "competence" has been identified as a goal for providers who serve our nation's warriors. In fact, this aspiration has been emphasized across multiple career domains within the healing professions and beyond. Is cultural competence the optimal goal? To what degree is this achievable? Can people who believe themselves to be culturally competent continue to have blind spots? How might reorienting towards cultural curiosity and cultural humility be helpful?

5. Working with warriors has helped me see that trust is the most important currency we can earn if we hope to support someone else.

> If you were to engage in a brutally honest self-assessment, would you say that others see you as trustworthy? Do they see you as dependable? In your experience and observation, are these qualities closely related or not? If they are, what is the cost of failing to follow through on what we commit to? What is the cost of being "flaky" in our social interactions? How does this impact the trust that others are willing to place in us?

Check out the handbook at the end of the book for further ways to apply this content.

2

WHAT IS STRENGTH, REALLY?

Just before I started exclusively working with veterans, I established a private practice during a one-year period in Florida before moving back to my home state of California. My private practice attracted well-educated, white-collar professionals. My patients showed up for all their appointments, eager to have a space to reflect on themselves and gain an additional professional perspective on a variety of psychological and situational challenges. They valued (and were willing to pay for) the opportunity to engage in therapy.

Around the same time as I launched my private practice, I collected data on a group of more than 1,200 well-educated women.[10] More than half of those surveyed had engaged in therapy at least once in their lives, and many reported having ongoing therapy sessions as part of their self-care. This was their thinking: "If I were to have a thorny tax problem, I would go to my accountant; in the same way, I consult with my therapist about the problems he or she has expertise to address." In fact, for many of them, it almost seemed that having regular therapy sessions was a mark of status ("I have a nice car, a beautiful home, and a top-shelf therapist.")

The picture changed when I started working with veterans. Often, they came to therapy reluctantly, at the strong urging of a concerned family member. Far from being excited about the opportunity to engage with me, the veteran was often looking for a good reason to never return. This contrast in cultures led me to consider the many ways in which supportive therapy is a countercultural experience for some groups of people, including those who have served in the military. Here are some of those ways.

As opposed to my civilian patients, typically, many veterans have had experiences that haven't given them reason to trust mental health providers. Specifically, veterans' interactions with mental health providers have often not been safe and supportive relationships — far from it. Their past providers have not so much had the veteran's back as they have been hired by the military to assess them for mission readiness.

This is not to say that military psychologists are not supportive of their patients. Because of the way roles are structured, however, many interactions with mental health providers in the military might effectively be characterized as a hunt for deficits that have high stakes for service members. For instance, psychologists in the military assess service members as part of routine predeployment screenings, fitness for duty assessments, med-board proceedings, and so on.

Their mission is to help service members "be all they can be" in a way that conforms to what the military needs. Again, this is not a criticism of these providers. It's just a statement of fact. Evaluations and many of the interactions with mental health providers in the military and first-responder setting have been strongly associated with negative outcomes or the possibility of them. No one was ever advanced or promoted due to a military psychologist's sterling review of their recently assessed shining mental health status.

In the context of these assessments, if mental health struggles are identified, there can be immediate professional and personal consequences for service members. Some may be put on profiles or flagged for duties other than those in their assigned military occupational specialty (MOS). Some may have their weapons removed if they are judged to be a risk to themselves or others.

When these kinds of things happen, service members may experience personal feelings of humiliation, especially if they are singled out for different treatment relative to others in the unit. In some cases, on the basis of these mental health evaluations, a service member's entire military career may be derailed if that service member is "med-boarded" or "medical-ed" out of the service.[11] In fact, Marines sometimes refer to mental health providers as "wizards" because they have the power to "make service members disappear."

There have been some positive movements to decrease stigma and increase mental health engagement. Increasingly, mental health providers are becoming embedded into military units. And some of these providers are docs. Some service members also have access to a limited scope of confidential supportive services with rotating providers called marriage family life counselors (MFLCs), who are contracted civilians outside of the military.

Despite these developments, however, the common thread in the military is that mental health providers serve in evaluative roles, primarily to ensure troop readiness. So, it should not surprise us that after discharge, many veterans are initially reluctant to trust their assigned mental health providers. This also helps explain the trust deficit mentioned in the previous chapter.

In 2004, Hoge and colleagues collected anonymous surveys from soldiers and Marines to learn about their attitudes towards mental health.[12] When considering engaging in mental health care:

- 65% reported that they would be seen as weak
- 63% felt that others would treat them differently
- 59% felt that members of their units would have less confidence in them
- 51% felt that leaders would blame them for the problem

- 50% felt that seeking therapy would harm their careers
- 41% felt that seeking care would be embarrassing

According to a report published by RAND in 2014,[13] while some of these numbers are declining, the highest level of concerns was reported by those who screened positive for mental health diagnoses — the very group that may benefit most from care.

From the viewpoint of the active duty service member, veteran, or first responder, there are vast differences between serving in the military or first-responder occupations and engaging in supportive mental health treatment. Understanding these will help us understand why veteran and first-responder patients might be hesitant to seek help. Consider the ways in which therapy is a countercultural proposition for these populations, as shown here:

Military Training Culture	Post-Military Counter-Cultural Needs
"Mission Readiness" is the priority	Restoring your health is the mission
Every action is judged	No one is here to judge you
Follow standard procedure	Think outside the box
It doesn't matter what you think	What you think matters and is critical to moving on
Strength is handling things on your own	Getting help makes you stronger in the end

First of all, there is a team versus individual focus and value system when comparing military and first-responder culture to the culture of therapy. Team values include a feeling that mission readiness is the priority. For example, in the military, every action is judged. Service members are literally treated as property of our government. Little care is given to how service members think or feel about a mission or military assignment. Service members cannot opt out of what they are assigned to do in the military. This is the way of our military.

The mission comes first, and the needs of the mission are weighed more heavily than the needs of the individuals involved. Individuals can feel less important in a culture with these values. This is not bad; it is just a part of military service. In fact, many who enter the military choose to enlist in order to feel connected to something that is bigger than themselves, and in so doing, they sacrifice many of their individual rights.

In contrast, in mental health treatment, the restoration of the patient's health *is* the mission. There is nothing more important. The patient is not being judged. Unconditional positive regard is a pillar of training for many therapists, and this humanistic value cuts across several approaches to therapy. Each patient is valued as a person who belongs to no one except himself or herself. Along these lines, the thoughts of each individual are not just important, but understanding and validating them in therapy is seen as a primary path to healing.

Second, there is a stark difference in the degree of autonomy felt as part of military service versus what a veteran might experience in treatment. In the military, service members follow orders. They do as they're told. There are standard operating procedures, and there is no choice in the matter. Following orders is vital to mission completion, and lives depend on it. The culture in our first responder populations is similar: individual choice and comfort are less important than the needs of the job. They are asked — sometimes daily — to risk their own safety, to maintain our safety when civil unrest breaks out.

Service members and first responders tend to take this attitude into their experience with mental health issues as well, believing for example that they should "suck it up" and get back to their jobs. In mental health treatment settings, veterans are asked to think critically as part of their recovery. Therapists often encourage their patients to be flexible in their thinking, to try to open their minds and think outside the box. The goal of therapy is often to empower patients to make their own choices about their lives. We may impress on them that it is their work in therapy, and their choice to focus on the issues that brought them to treatment, that will provide them with the lives they want to live. Personal choice is essential in most mental health treatment protocols, regardless of a therapist's training background.

Finally, the definition of "strength" that is upheld in warrior culture is very different from the way that strength is viewed in therapy. In warrior culture, strength is defined as perseverance in the face of physical, mental, and emotional pain. In fact, this kind of strength is not only valued, but it is also expected and required.

For example, service members believe in slogans like "Pain is weakness leaving the body." They believe that their minds are strong enough to conquer pain, physical and emotional, by compartmentalizing and essentially ignoring pain. They are taught that being strong means dealing with things by themselves, and that asking for help makes them weak. Military service members often joke that the treatment for any problem one might have is to "take two Motrin (vitamin M), and it will go away on its own in time."

In contrast, in treatment with a mental health professional, patients are guided to understand that they are actually very brave for admitting they need help. Pretending a problem doesn't exist is often easier than confronting it. Being humble enough to admit to a problem requires strength of character. Successfully addressing a problem requires the internal will to adapt and overcome, and to persist in the face of obstacles.

Changing habits and patterns is hard for all of us, and it can be physically and emotionally painful. As we will see in a later chapter, repairing damage that has been done to one's relationships may actually be harder than walking into an ambush in the combat zone.

Providers do their best to help their patients alleviate emotional pain during the process of treatment. But sometimes we have to confront painful experiences directly. In some cases, the best way through obstacles is to charge straight through them and take the metaphorical hill. We may have to break down before we can become stronger, just as muscles get stronger after muscle fibers are torn. At other times, we need to learn to live in the pain. Viewed in this light, it becomes easy to see how avoiding behavioral health issues is the easier, more comfortable path, while getting help takes courage.

UNIVERSAL PRINCIPLES I LEARNED FROM WORKING WITH WARRIORS

1. ***If you want to reduce stigma, you must redefine strength in ways that fit with the cultural values of those whom you are working to support.***

   Helping people see a new definition of strength decreases stigma. For example, military service members are given specific training challenges to help them evolve in valued ways. So, we can reduce stigma by translating these concepts into the work of therapy and other forms of personal growth after discharge. By doing so, we give voice to a new definition of strength — a new mission (or crucible) that will shape the next chapter in their lives. We can tell them that in therapy:

   a. Restoring their health is the priority.
   b. They can draw on their proven ability to adapt and overcome.
   c. The goal is to think creatively and outside the box.
   d. What they think matters and is critical in their recovery.

   By reframing the therapeutic process as their mission, we align with their desire to take on challenges to get stronger. When viewed from this angle, it is not difficult to frame the challenge of growth in a way that meets veterans' strengths and fits their existing cultural values. For instance, I might say something like:

   > Okay, so we agree that avoiding facing the challenges we're discussing might feel easier and more comfortable. Showing up for therapy, not just today, but for whatever sessions we agree to schedule in the future, is the harder and braver choice. Therapy then can be seen as your next challenge. I am here to walk with you and help you make progress on the goals you set for yourself.

> You will tell me about what changes you want to see in your life, and I will advise you as you navigate the challenges to making progress on your goals. In the process, you will use your ability to adapt and overcome. Also, as in the military, you will learn new things about yourself, find out what you are truly capable of, and will be stronger in the end for taking the harder path.

Through simple statements like these, we can reinforce these ideas in our patients. We can be the health-care providers who change our patients' perceptions of mental health.

2. ***Stigma weakens when we get ambivalence out in the open as soon as possible.***

Unspoken reluctance to participate in therapy is like the invisible, submerged part of an iceberg that can grind treatment to a halt before it even begins. Unacknowledged ambivalence (or lack of buy-in, as those in the business world might say) is a hidden force that causes many important and innovative efforts to grind to a halt. For this reason, it is critical to get ambivalence out in the open as early as possible in the process of working towards a common goal.

As I have said, many veterans are scanning for a reason to never come back, but if you openly acknowledge this ambivalence, you have a much better chance of building trust. Once ambivalence is out in the open, you will be able to directly address the thoughts and feelings that can be real barriers to any goal-driven process. As shown in the previous example, when offering therapy to a veteran, you can do this in a way that emphasizes existing strengths. On the other hand, failing to address unspoken ambivalence can directly lead patients to drop out of care[14] or to other valuable efforts and projects suddenly losing momentum.

3. ***Anxiety decreases when past learning is tapped for growth in new challenges.***

   To help reduce anxiety about taking on new challenges, it helps to think about how past learning can support a successful outcome. For example, in the case of veterans and behavioral health treatment, military experience can be a direct asset in therapy. Specifically, in the military, service members learn how to work as a team, so veterans are used to working on challenges in partnership with others.

   We can help veterans reconnect with their tribe, and if we become their doc, then we ourselves can become a trusted extension of that tribe. When we do this, we move the therapy relationship away from an isolated, one-on-one consultation (which can feel countercultural) into a form that gives us real traction.

   Military training also repeatedly emphasizes persistence in the face of obstacles, something similar to what Angela Duckworth writes about in her book *Grit: The Power of Passion and Perseverance.*[15] If we can tap into the grit that our service members learned in the military, we will help them achieve astounding successes.

   What I have witnessed is nothing short of miraculous when warfighters turn that "never, ever quit" attitude towards their goals for growth. Marriages have been reignited, badly damaged relationships with children have been healed, and many of my patients have accomplished incredible success. They have gone from being homeless to being admitted to our nation's top universities. They have been elected into positions of civic leadership. One even traveled to China to present his innovative ideas to global business leaders.

   Therapy can become the next evolution, the crucible that makes them stronger in the end. As they push through barrier after barrier, sometimes using a full-out aggressive approach, they redefine their limits and learn what they are truly capable of.

To emphasize this model, I teamed up with a veteran peer to share this message with new patients. We developed new patient orientation groups ("new patient briefing") and a group called "Boot Camp Stories" to help patients develop comfort with the VA clinic where I used to work.

Military training and therapy are sometimes very similar. For example, military training and in vivo exposures to anxiety as part of treatment can help us redefine our current limits, and learn who we are and what we are capable of. When seen through this lens, therapy doesn't feel so foreign. It is just another growth opportunity for those who are willing to take on the challenge.

4. ***Empowering others to overcome challenges means putting them in the driver's seat.***

We empower people by putting them in the driver's seat. I've found that veterans and first responders are often concerned that therapy will be disempowering. The new patient briefing groups that I developed and co-hosted with a veteran peer gave us an opportunity to strategically address this concern, to show them that they will be in the driver's seat.

As bodybuilders know, what happens in session is often much less important than what happens between sessions. Each individual has the power and the ultimate responsibility to make changes in his or her life. Patients should neither put their therapists on a pedestal nor see us as wizards (in any sense of the word). We have expertise to lend to the process of growth, but they must remain in the driver's seat. To explain this, I told them:

> Let's say that I were a bodybuilding coach — not a psychologist — and you come to me and tell me that you want to compete in a professional bodybuilding contest. So, I give you recipes to make, probably with lots of raw eggs and whey protein in them,

> and give you a workout regimen. You show up week after week and tell me that you are frustrated with your progress. I ask you if you have done the workouts or made the lifestyle changes between our sessions and you say, "Well, no."
>
> In the same way, in therapy, we might reach some insights and put our heads together to come up with a plan for change, but you need to invest the time and energy between sessions to bring about the changes you want for yourself.

This simple analogy helped them understand their responsibility in therapy, which both empowered them and helped them to see therapists in a different light, as advisors, not saviors. As we will see in Chapter 5, shifting the therapist role well away from the "savior" realm becomes especially critical when shame is a third party in the room — a fox in their gut, in other words.

QUESTIONS FOR REFLECTION AND APPLICATION

1. Mental health providers who serve in military contexts have a dual role: They support individual wellness and assess for troop readiness. As a result of this evaluative element in these treatment relationships, some veterans may not have an existing model for a purely supportive treatment relationship. When people in our lives are reluctant to trust us, might there be a past experience or a string of past experiences that can help us understand their ambivalence? How can we identify this in a respectful way?

2. Many of the veterans I have served have been very reluctant to engage in therapy, at least initially. When we sense ambivalence in someone else, what does it take to bring their ambivalence into the room? If we haven't yet developed trust with them, how can we bring this up in a way that is most likely to be effective?

3. Among the veterans I have treated, it has been critical to empower them in their own healing process. Sometimes, despite our best intentions, we take more control than we should in the healing journey of those we aim to support. When does supporting someone cross over into taking too much responsibility for their outcomes? What are some cues that we have fallen into this trap?

4. Many of my veteran patients already possess the skills they need to meet the challenges in their lives. In such cases, my work has been geared towards helping them migrate existing strengths to their goals for growth. To apply the principles discussed in this chapter to your own personal growth, are there challenges in your own life that might be well met with strengths you have developed in the past? What would happen if you sat down and mapped out how your existing strengths might help you achieve the outcome(s) you want in a future area of growth?

5. The hard thing to do can also be the brave thing, but that doesn't always mean that the hard thing to do is always the *right* thing in every case. How can we tell when something feels *hard but right?* How does this feel different from when our fear instructs us for good reason to take a different path? What cues can we use to help us tell the difference between anxiety that is an obstacle to overcome in order to grow versus anxiety that comes from a wise place?

Don't forget to check the handbook at the end of the book for further ways to apply this content.

3

THE MYTH OF THE BROKEN ONES

In a VA clinic where I worked many years ago, there were two bathrooms just next to each other. They shared a wall. One was the staff bathroom and one was the patient bathroom. They were pretty much the same, except for the signs on their doors. One week, some of us began to notice urine splatters on the seat in the staff bathroom. This became a regular thing. It may sound like a small thing to have to wipe up pee drops on the seat before using the restroom, but it is a chronically irritating thing that can make you feel helpless and disrespected.

Notes started appearing on the wall of the bathroom, initially humorous in nature. Someone probably accessed Pinterest before posting a good-natured sign that said, "Our aim is to keep this bathroom clean. Gentlemen, your aim will help. Stand closer, it's shorter than you think. Ladies, please remain seated for your entire performance." The issue came up in all-staff emails and during staff meetings. As weeks turned into months and the problem persisted, the tension ratcheted up in the clinic. One day, I walked into the staff bathroom to find the following note.

> Please do not urinate on the seat. Others use the STAFF bathroom. If you urinate on the seat, please wash it down with soap and water, and dry the seat off with a dry, clean paper towel.
>
> Patients are not supposed to use this bathroom for the reason above. Use the patient bathroom and make your mess over there! Thank you.

So, if we're analyzing the assumptions in this note, we might surmise that:

1. Veteran patients are slovenly and tend to make a mess of a commode.

2. Staff and patients are separated for the protection and comfort of the staff given point #1.

3. This separation is the natural order of things: people in the two distinct tribes should pee in ways that are equal, but separate.

The funny thing about this story is that, in the end, the culprit was not a veteran, but rather a very highly educated staff member. Sometimes, the culture gap — which is also a trust and respect gap — surfaces in surprising ways like this, but most of the time, it comes out in ways that are unintentional.

Take for example all the questions we ask patients when they enroll in behavioral health care. Asking new patients to fill out a stack of symptom measures ("Please check off any symptoms you are experiencing") has become common practice in recent years, not only in the VA, but also in many health-care systems. In the last several years, the way we practice in mental health has moved in the direction of primary care, with lots of required screening measures embedded in scheduled appointments.

Providers in either primary care or mental health settings can't just ignore these "clinical reminders"; one is expected to complete them as part of one's required duties. Performance evaluations and peer reviews incorporate an assessment of each provider's "fidelity" (a polite way to say "compliance") to this model of care.

Asking questions about symptoms assists providers in understanding possible targets for treatment. Brief assessment measures are used in theory to prevent us from missing something important, like suicidal thoughts and feelings (this assumes patients will answer our questions candidly, which may be unlikely if trust hasn't been established.) However, there are some serious downsides to this approach to practice.

In the case of veterans, there are at least three overlooked problems with this approach to engaging them in care.

First, it undeniably changes the tone of a first appointment when a provider and/or a new patient is compelled to immediately answer several symptom measures. As I previously pointed out, veterans are used to being repeatedly screened and assessed in the military, and these assessments are associated with a variety of potentially negative consequences. So, all the symptom-focused measures we give them after discharge continue this pattern of behavior. This makes it harder to help veterans differentiate between supportive therapy and an evaluative psych assessment.

Also, when we are sitting at a computer completing symptom measures, we are not sitting with our patients. Our eyes are focused on a computer screen, not on the people in front of us. Here are a few examples of very common statements made by veterans who have felt disrespected as a result of some of my fellow providers' approaches to practice:

> "He drilled me with questions the whole time, never letting me speak."
>
> "She never made eye contact with me the whole f-cking time we met."
>
> "She sat at her computer the whole time with her back to me and the door open."

The ability to sit with our patients, make eye contact, and not be so rushed that we make them feel like a burden to us is something we should protect. We should be thoughtful before rushing headlong into making the practice of mental health increasingly similar to that of primary care in managed care systems. When engaging veterans and first responders in any given health-care setting, the heavy inclusion of symptom measures during clinical sessions absolutely has an impact on our ability to connect with our patients and show them what supportive care feels like.

Second, in the context of showing respect, symptom-focused intakes immediately construct a hierarchical relationship that puts the provider in a one-up position and the veteran in a one-down position. The therapy relationship is already constructed in a way that likely feels hierarchical to patients because it is a one-sided disclosure.

This practice highlights a kind of relative rank during the critical first points of contact. The provider is set up to provide help, ask questions about problems the veteran has, and render expert assessment. Doctors are comfortable with this arrangement, but docs are often uneasy with this setup. Why? Because this behavior says "I outrank you" to the veterans who present for care. This is problematic because many veterans have experiences in the military that are tied to a good amount of pride (and usually, the good kind of pride).

Many veterans have been placed in roles of incredible responsibility at extremely young ages. They have made decisions that carried life-and-death stakes for fireteams, units, platoons, and so on. Some of my patients have told me that they felt a godlike power in changing the course of large groups of oppressed people or even the future of entire nations. In a particularly insightful TED Talk,[16] Sebastian Junger describes how service members are empowered in their role as warriors but then return to a society that strips them of their rank and position.

When we integrate these insights, it makes sense that many veterans and first responders would not want to find themselves effectively outranked by someone who has not had these kinds of experiences. Many warriors do not initially value civilian providers as people with learning and expertise to offer. Instead, they see us initially as people who have had our heads in the books, who are lacking in gritty, real-world experiences. So, if we want to engage warriors in treatment, we need to be thoughtful about setting up a relationship that suggests we outrank them.

Finally, asking only about problems and symptoms communicates a way of seeing our warriors that aligns with the myth that they are somehow "broken people." American Grit's John Fannin explains, "There is a myth that veterans are broken. That war has somehow destroyed the mind, body, and soul. The idea that we as veterans are dysfunctional and cannot reintegrate back into society is absolute garbage. … Society has this stigma about warriors, that what we do somehow rips apart our humanity and damages us beyond repair. … For too long the community, the tribe has been told by outsiders and by each other, that we are broken." When speaking to a group of Marines at the Marine's Memorial Club in San Francisco, General Mattis once said, "If we tell our veterans enough that they are damaged goods, they may actually start believing it."[17]

You may be thinking, hold on, though. Isn't that the function of a mental health provider — to identify and treat the problems that cause suffering? To this question, I would respond that the higher-order function of any healer is to build trust, which allows us to get the real story, and engage people in a process of growth. If this is our goal, then we need to engage in more holistic, respectful assessment. To illustrate, consider these sample items, which are part of the PCL-5, a standard assessment of post-traumatic stress that is used widely across systems of care:

- ✓ Having strong negative beliefs about yourself, other people, or the world (for example, having thoughts such as: I am bad; there is something seriously wrong with me; no one can be trusted; the world is completely dangerous)?
- ✓ Blaming yourself or someone else for the stressful experience or what happened after it?
- ✓ Having strong negative feelings such as fear, horror, anger, guilt, or shame?[18]

These questions align with a type of interaction that amounts to a "hunt for deficits" with new patients. They also require disclosure of shame-based experiences very early in a treatment relationship. Asking these kinds of questions in isolation communicates an expectation of veterans' functioning. When I realized this, I created a supplemental measure to provide a more balanced, holistic assessment of each new patient on my caseload. Here are some of the items I added:

- ✓ Missing the adrenaline rush of combat and frequently wishing you were back in the combat zone?
- ✓ Feeling an intensely pleasurable feeling in your body when you hear the sounds or see the sights of combat? (for example, the sound of heavy artillery being fired in a war video)?
- ✓ Increased interest in playing graphic war video games or watching graphic war movies that remind you of the stressful event(s) you experienced?
- ✓ Wishing someone would pick a physical fight because it would feel good to fight?
- ✓ Feeling very close to those you served with in the military in a way that is hard to imagine with others you used to feel close to?

I created this supplemental measure with several strategic goals. First, I wanted to communicate my understanding that military service can involve peak life experiences, including the rush of being in combat. Warfighters leave the military with a complicated array of feelings as well as altered identities. Negative experiences are often intermixed with positive experiences. Consider this piece of writing, given to me by a veteran who has not been my patient:

> I find myself craving what I sometimes couldn't wait to get away from … it bonds with your DNA, and there is no shaking it. None. It's you. It defines who you are … or at least a portion of who you are. … Would I change it? Not a thing. Taking lives, losing friends, sharing the fear and exhilaration, suffering through the heat and boredom, missing family and holidays. It makes me who I am, and I love it. All of it … on some level.

Because the experiences of combat create such a complicated set of reactions, I wanted to create a measure that would help them identify a set of experiences, both positive and negative, that are common — and therefore *normal* — for those exposed to combat. This sets a tone of respect and helps decrease stigma. These insights can help all of us connect more fully to the veterans in our lives. Rather than assuming that they have been damaged by their time in the military, we can ask about their peak experiences. If they trust us, we are sure to hear some awe-inspiring stories.

Moreover, asking about experiences like "missing the adrenaline rush of combat" or "wishing someone would pick a physical fight because it would feel good to fight" immediately expands the range for potential discussions. By speaking to these types of experiences directly, and acknowledging that aggressive thoughts, feelings, and impulses are far from unmentionable, I communicated that we can talk about all of their experiences, not just the parts that may lead to night sweats. Items like "feeling indestructible given what you have survived" or "feeling very close to those you served with in the military in a way that is hard to imagine with others you used to feel close to" helped to equalize our roles. These items implicitly reference strengths often acquired in the military.

One of my colleagues once told me that he said to a patient, "Hey, man, let me tell you, if there were an active shooter in the building, I'd be totally freaked out and take my instructions from you on what to do." I thought this was really smart, so I designed some questions to relay this equalizing sentiment.

Docs don't reinforce the myth of the broken veteran in their approach because they see it as a myth. They don't see veterans as damaged goods, but as individuals who are generally capable and resourceful. A doc partners with veterans to help them work towards whatever goals they set for themselves. And while docs have skills to offer, they communicate that veterans also bring special skills and a strength that is often battle tested.

By adopting this approach, regardless of our role, we can have deeper, more meaningful conversations with the warriors in our lives.

Creating and leading with a more holistic assessment shaped my practice in ways that were invaluable. Responses to my supplemental questions helped me discern the nature of a given veteran's reluctance to engage in treatment.[19] Once I had a good read on the source of their reluctance, we were able to openly examine it. For example, sometimes the sacred is bound up with the pain. In these discussions, I told combat veterans that there is nothing treatment can do to remove or weaken their memories of any of the experiences they hold sacred.

For example, several veterans did not want to stop having nightmares or intrusive memories because this was the only time they were able to commune with some of their fallen brothers. They had an unspoken fear that if therapy were to help them process these experiences, then the memories would fade, and they would lose contact with people they loved like family.

So, when they heard that my goal in therapy was to help them to *reconnect* with their fallen brothers in ways that would be meaningful, more frequent, and much less painful, they were able to open up more fully to the process of treatment. They also learned that I was never going to tell them to get over it, as no one should ever say to someone who is grieving (more on this in Chapter 6).

The practice of offering medication to veterans is also tied to the myth of the broken veteran. Medications can be very helpful for some veterans, but this conversation is a delicate one. Veterans may react with anger if they are offered medication early in the process by providers they do not know or trust. Several of my patients explained that being offered medications makes them feel shuffled off or communicates that there is no hope that they will improve without medication.

What does "right" look like? It looks like the practice of prescribing docs who make sure to communicate that (a) medication is optional; (b) medication may help optimize the benefits of talk therapy in some cases; (c) medication may be time limited; and (d) staying on medication (or not) is an open question that will be continuously reviewed.

If we were to implement some of these suggestions for building trust and better engaging our warriors (and other patients) in treatment, how might we measure success? At present, across systems of care, both in the VA and in civilian health-care settings, we commonly use utilization and time to first appointment as ways to quantify access to care. For example, in the VA, we measure what percent of veterans have accessed at least one appointment at a VA clinic (around 50% to 60%)[20] or the time it takes for new patients to get a first appointment. It's good to measure population-level utilization and time to first appointment, but what if we also looked at the conversion of first appointments into meaningful, ongoing treatment?

Given that research on the population at large shows that 70% of people who drop out of mental health treatment do so after just the first or second visit,[21] I wonder, how many veterans attend a fourth, fifth, or sixth session with their providers? How many drop out after just one or two sessions? My theory is that this would probably be a proxy measure of the doctors and docs in a given health-care system; the data would likely show that treatment would generally unfold with some providers, while others would have relatively high rates of transfer requests and drop out from care.

UNIVERSAL PRINCIPLES I LEARNED FROM WORKING WITH WARRIORS

1. ***Disrespect can be communicated even when this is not the intention of the communicator.***

   Disrespect is communicated in largely unintentional ways — with the heavy focus on symptom assessment, in the tone of sessions, and in conversations about medication prescriptions. There is one other major area where unintended disrespect is frequently communicated: safety and ownership of firearms. This is such a big topic that it needs its own full chapter (coming next in Chapter 4). Suffice it to say that in many of our current approaches to discussing firearm safety practices with veterans, many of us are peeing all over the seat we are asking veterans to sit on.

2. ***The socialization of certain professions and the way systems of care are set up can put people into roles that may be unhelpful to building trust.***

   There are often invisible forces at play in how people are educated and how systems of care are set up that prevent healers from connecting with those they serve. For instance, clinical detachment is emphasized in many graduate programs. Many therapists are taught not to share personal opinions or openly express personal thoughts and feelings. We are taught to avoid "unprofessional" displays of humor (let alone dropping an f-bomb in the context of a therapy session).[22] Many of us were also trained in reflective listening, paraphrasing what our patients say to help them gain new perspective, without revealing anything of ourselves in the process. The intention of guiding us this way is to emphasize that therapy is not about us as healers; instead, our role is to serve our patients.

While this guidance is well intended, it can backfire in practice. What this creates is a relationship in which one person takes all the risks and makes all the disclosures, and the other observes and reflects in a relatively detached way. In other words, by creating therapy relationships that align with classical training models, we may be setting up a relationship that is comfortable to us as therapists, given our training and civilian social norms, but which may be deeply uncomfortable for many of our patients.

Rather than feeling cared for, our patients may feel scrutinized, judged, or put under a spotlight. Rather than feeling that we are getting a thorough assessment of the problem to help us make good decisions about treatment, our patient may feel psychologically dissected. And feeling psychologically dissected is the farthest thing from feeling respected.

3. ***There are higher-order functions for those in healing roles; beyond evaluating and treating problems, there is the critical work of showing respect and building trust.***

This point bears repeating: Unless we can build trust, we will never hear what we need to understand. Veterans, first responders, and perhaps people in general, are much less inclined to form a connection with someone whose behavior presumes a trust that has not yet been earned. It is important for us to get better and better at precisely evaluating situations — whether in the mental health field or in the business world — but we have to consider the ways in which our increasingly dominant focus on data collection impacts the higher-order functions of our professions.

4. ***If our gut tells us that a standard procedure isn't the best approach, there are often creative ways to better align our practice with our values as healers.***

   Because of how systems are set up, we may have to comply with some approaches we would not choose otherwise. We can't just outright rebel and fail to complete required aspects of our jobs. However, when our gut tells us that the standard procedure has consequences for patient care, customer service, or workforce well-being, there are often creative ways to supplement what we do to help alleviate the issues we observe.

   Leaders among us need to be thoughtful about the unintended consequences of standardizing practices to such an extent that we change the nature of what we hope to create. In mental health work, the thing that needs to be protected is the trust and the authentic, cooperative relationship between healers and those they serve.

QUESTIONS FOR REFLECTION AND APPLICATION

1. If you are a civilian, how do you see our nation's warriors? How many deep and trusting relationships do you currently have with those who have served in the military? What perceptions do you have about veterans as a group? Is this any different from how you view our first responders? Within first responder populations (police, firefighters, emergency medical personnel, emergency dispatchers), does this perception vary between subgroups?

2. The myth of the broken veteran is one example of how the stories we tell about groups of people can create feelings of shame, even when they are not true. For instance, in the case of veterans, despite the widespread perception that many veterans struggle with symptoms of post-traumatic stress, research suggests that the vast majority of veterans do not develop PTSD.[23] Why do these kinds of myths persist, even in the face of widely available data? What will it take to shift damaging narratives like this one?

3. How can we as citizens who are supportive of our veterans have healthier, more informed conversations about the full range of experiences in the military? What situations in our own lives can help us relate — even a little bit — to some of the positive experiences of those who have served in the military? For example, are there times when we have enjoyed aggressive behavior (e.g., while sparring in a martial arts class) or felt that we would do anything to protect someone we love (e.g., consider what a parent might instinctively do if their child were threatened by a stranger).

4. Do you agree that the higher-order function of healers in our society is to build trust and create authentic relationships? How can a data-driven approach fit with this? When and how should we assess problems?

5. When you think about the development of health care systems in the places where you live and work, are there areas where it feels like we are moving fast in a direction that doesn't feel right? Where do you notice this? What kinds of modifications might help balance the problems you observe?

Check out the handbook at the end of the book for further ways to apply this content.

4

A LOADED CONVERSATION

Can physical objects become extensions of our identity? Can they represent values that are both deeply personal and strongly tied to how we view our role in society? To understand how to make a skillful approach in discussing firearm safety practices, we need to understand why our current approaches to this conversation may feel so disrespectful to many veterans, first responders, and other firearm owners.

Military[24] training is the antidote to feelings of personal vulnerability. Training helps service members acquire the will and confidence to dominate our country's enemies. Even those in the military who are not in combat roles are taught how to use firearms as weapons. So, there is a sizable group of people each year who are taught to use firearms for protective defense and aggressive military offense. For those in combat roles, such as infantry Marines ("grunts") and frontline soldiers, the relationship with their firearm is especially important. It is the primary source of protection — for themselves and their brothers- and sisters-in-arms.

During advanced combat training, a firearm effectively becomes an extension of the self. A service member's firearm is to be skillfully wielded, constantly well maintained, and readily available. Service members are not only provided with a tool that can save their life and the lives of those they share a foxhole with. They are also invested with the trust of society to use this tool for the defense of what is right and good.

I would imagine that for many combat service members, the issue of a firearm might feel a bit like King Arthur receiving the sword Excalibur. For many, this is a sacred rite of passage, a pathway to adulthood. In fact, the process of receiving a firearm and learning to use it in the military context may be the closest thing we have to being "knighted" in modern American culture.

As they grow into their roles and learn to skillfully use their firearms, many combat veterans come to see themselves as "sheepdogs," positioned to take out the wolves (e.g., terrorists) that threaten the herd. But this analogy makes everyone else a sheep, which I don't like because I think there are many ways to be a warrior, beyond wielding physical weapons. In fact, as an aside, helping veterans see that they can be warriors in different ways beyond just the combat role — they can use their will and their education and *all that they are* to defend their sacred values throughout their life is critical to helping them make a successful transition after the military.

In any case, by virtue of their training and the values they hold sacred, combat veterans see themselves as precisely the group of people who *should* be armed in case criminal activity, civil unrest, or a zombie uprising should break out. Because of their combat exposure, many veterans are more in tune than most of us with the primal human drive to dominate and overturn social order for individual or corporate gain.

When things do take a sudden violent turn, veterans will often take it upon themselves, unarmed or otherwise, to patrol dangerous neighborhoods and protect those without military skills. As a group, I have generally found veterans to be protective by nature, and I, for one, feel safer knowing that several of my patients are looking out for all of us. I think others would feel the same if they knew the kinds of vital roles many of our veterans assume in society, whether in civilian defense companies, in disaster response operations, or simply by standing up to neighborhood bullies.

At the same time, several researchers and clinicians have expressed urgent and understandable concern about the connection between firearms and veteran suicide. Firearms are the primary go-to method of suicide deaths among members of the American military.[31] They are highly lethal: 85% of attempts with firearms lead to completed suicides, while just 2% of poisoning or overdose attempts lead to the same.[26] And firearms are very dangerous in combination with the rapid onset of self-destructive urges.[27]

To this point, a number of research studies suggest that periods of acute suicidal urges may be relatively short in duration. For instance, a study of more than twenty-six thousand college and graduate school students suggested that a typical period of acute suicidal thinking lasted less than a day for over half of those who were suicidal at any time.[28] Another study of eighty-two patients in a psychiatric university hospital showed an even shorter duration of acute suicidality; just under half of participants reported a span of ten minutes or less for their suicidal process.[29] Similarly, in another study, 40% of the sample considered self-harm for ten minutes or less before making an attempt.[30]

In these critical moments, firearms initially intended for protection can suddenly become weapons of self-destruction for those who own them. Research suggests that 90% of those who die by suicide with a firearm had no prior suicide attempts by any method.[31] There is also compelling research to show that restricted access to firearms can have an immediate positive impact on suicide rates.[32] In a study conducted in Israel, where weekend firearm suicides among military service members were noted as a troubling pattern, a small change in policy to require that IDF soldiers leave their weapons on base over weekends resulted in a 40% decline in the annual number of suicides.[33]

Because I am committed to approaching every topic in this book with honesty, it must be said that there is real cause for concern that among *some* within the veteran and first responder populations, firearms can become weapons of self-destruction when emotional, psychological, and physical pain becomes overwhelming. As Thomas Joiner's research has shown,[34] military training can habituate service members to acts of violence, which may remove barriers to self-harm that might otherwise present a greater obstacle.

Those in combat roles have had long practice in quelling their fear and stemming their adrenaline response to using firearms. They have developed muscle memory for how to fire a weapon. Those of us who are less experienced with firearms may initially have a fearful or aversive response to holding a firearm, but for veterans and some first responders, especially those with firearm expertise, the associations are most often positive; in most cases, a firearm is mentally categorized as a friend rather than a foe. So, when a veteran fixates on the notion that he is a threat or burden to those he loves, there is a real danger that a firearm can become a weapon for self-destruction.

Based on these lines of research, systems of care that treat large groups of veterans have focused on access to lethal means as a key target for addressing veteran suicide. The current standard practice is to assess suicidal ideation early and often. When veterans respond to broad screening questions that suggest a potentially elevated risk of suicide, clinicians are urged to initiate discussions that would prompt veteran patients to reduce access to means, including firearms. Here is the specific language used to inform the current standard practice:

> The clinician should routinely ask whether the veteran has access to a firearm (such as a handgun, rifle or shotgun), whether or not it is considered a "method of choice" and make arrangements for securing the weapon … . An optimal plan would be to restrict the veterans' access to a highly lethal method by having it safely stored by a designated, responsible person — usually a family member or close friend, or even the police (Simon, 2007).[35]

To civilians who care about and for veterans, this seems like a no-brainer, and like so many efforts made to support veterans, these efforts are well intended.

Unfortunately, our current approaches can seriously backfire. To many veterans, asking questions about firearm ownership feels intrusive at best, and possibly deeply disrespectful. Asking the question can immediately rupture the therapeutic relationship and may lead many veterans to drop out of treatment entirely. How do I know? Because I expressed interest in learning what veterans *really* think about this topic, and a veteran who wanted to help me get to the truth asked a group of seventy fellow veterans.

Who Is Asking Matters

Unlike the other studies cited above, which were conducted by career researchers, the survey that follows was sourced directly from college-enrolled veterans across three campuses at the request of a veteran who is known and respected within the veteran community. Both methods have their advantages, but when it comes to sensitive questions, who is asking matters.

Research studies that are run through institutions, universities, or the government often elicit anxiety in veteran respondents. Whether or not there is factual basis for concern, in my observation, veterans are likely to inhibit their responses when polled by any of these entities. Institutional distrust ("How do I know this isn't being tracked?") can be a substantial barrier to open disclosure. This distrust is understandable given that when veterans were service members, their most private information was actively tracked in the military.

This barrier of institutional distrust is removed when a fellow veteran asks the questions, which may make this relatively casual inquiry of seventy veterans our best window into what veterans really think on the issue of firearm safety discussions. When asked, "Are you likely to be open and truthful about whether you own firearms if asked by a provider you do not know well," over half (53%) said "probably not" or "no." However, the most critical finding in this poll, and the one that is most concerning, is that half of the veterans said that they would probably drop out of treatment if a clinician they did not know well asked them whether they own a firearm.

The way these seventy veterans responded should give us all serious pause for reflection. If trust is the strongest currency we can earn, we should ask ourselves about the cost of driving the therapeutic relationship towards potential dishonesty. The perception that a clinician may have the agenda or ability to remove a firearm (even if this perception is factually inaccurate)[36] can be a substantial barrier to care.

Compelling clinicians by standard policy and practice to have this discussion up front, before developing trust, widens the trust gap at precisely the time when we need to connect and build trust with our patients. In fact, asking questions about firearm ownership may even increase suicide risk if this leads veterans to avoid seeking care in the first place. Before considering other approaches, let's seek to understand the issue more fully. Psychologically, asking them to remove their firearms creates intense feelings of vulnerability on two levels: (1) the immediate physical level and (2) the psychological level.

Physical and Psychological Vulnerability

The driving reason many veterans and first responders own firearms is to have a way to protect themselves and their families "in case something goes down." Many have seen firsthand the primitive underbelly of civilization. They are keenly aware of the ongoing struggle for dominance between humans across societies. Many have directly witnessed the violence we are capable of, and it is seared into their memories. As Karl Marlantes, author of *What It Is Like to Go to War* has said:

> One of the things I learned in the war is that we're not the top species on the planet because we're nice. We are a very aggressive species. It is in us. And people talk about how the military turns kids into killing machines ... I will always argue that it is just finishing school. What

> we do within civilization is that we learn to inhibit and rope in these aggressive tendencies.[37]

Many veterans share the same understanding and, for this reason, want their personal firearm to be readily accessible. As Navy SEAL Commander Rorke Denver once said during a fireside chat, "We're always planning for the zombie apocalypse to happen."[38] Commonly, veterans store a weapon intended for self-protection close at hand when they sleep — often in a bedside table. They want them nearby for physical protection, and the thought of losing access to their firearm creates feelings of physical vulnerability. Anyone who thinks otherwise has not heard enough veterans say things like, "I can't sleep unless I have my [Glock][39] next to the bed."

In addition to physical vulnerability, questions about firearms raise the specter of psychological vulnerability, which may not be fully appreciated by those who engage them in firearm safety conversations. In the military context, taking a firearm away from someone is a power move that is done by a person with higher rank. The act has meaning that cuts to the core of a military service member's identity. Removal of a firearm signifies that that service member is not deemed competent to retain firearm privileges.

One way to look at it is that this action effectively strips them of "knighthood." In such a scenario, a service member may feel shamed as loss of a firearm signifies loss of a function that is highly valued in the military — the ability to protect themselves and others.

Social consequences also may be swift and severe. That service member may be flagged as a self-harm risk or "put on a profile." They may be suddenly pulled out of their unit (their tribe) and assigned different duties. This is often deeply humiliating to them. They can become isolated and may feel suddenly irrelevant. This can directly increase suicidal ideation to the degree that they begin to think of themselves as a burden or a liability. So, when a civilian provider (in a VA or elsewhere) asks about reducing access to firearms, this emotionally loaded meaning can be triggered, and create sudden and intense feelings of both physical and psychological vulnerability.

UNIVERSAL PRINCIPLES I LEARNED FROM WORKING WITH WARRIORS

1. ***When it comes to sensitive topics, you can be bold to the degree that you have earned trust.***

   If you have established a healthy level of trust with someone, you can typically be bolder in your approach around sensitive topics. For example, if a veteran trusts you, she already knows that you have her back. There is a pattern of supportive behavior that has allowed her to see you as Doc or a fellow member of her Tribe. So, perhaps you might say something like the following:

   > I read a study recently that said firearms are sometimes used for self-destructive purposes in a moment of sudden impulsivity, in many cases by people with no previous history of suicide attempts. Since you are really battling with your demons right now, I want to make sure this doesn't happen. Do you own a firearm?

   In this scenario, she is likely to see this as your way of looking out for her. In the absence of trust, on the other hand, a patient — whether veteran or civilian — is likely to filter the communication through a different lens. When trust is low, there is a real possibility of shifting the therapy relationship from one that feels supportive to one that feels driven by self-protective motives.

2. ***If you are not credible, say so.***

   One major reason why firearm safety conversations with veterans are not productive is that many civilian clinicians do not have any credibility to discuss firearms in the first place. For example, many civilian clinicians refer to firearms as "guns," a term that veterans generally do not use. Many civilian providers, even those who work every day with veterans, don't understand the conceptual difference between a "firearm" and a "weapon" within military culture.[40] Using the wrong basic language in these conversations displays ignorance and heightens the cultural disconnect veterans may feel with some clinicians.

Based on the feedback I received from my colleagues, some clinicians may feel anxiety holding a firearm, even an unloaded one. It follows that they would not be able to credibly demonstrate how to correctly use a firearm lock or to thoughtfully weigh the safety considerations involved in giving up a form of personal protection in order to decrease the risk of suicide.

In contrast, veterans, especially combat veterans, have had extensive training on the safe use of firearms. They are seasoned professionals with deep expertise in this area. So, having people without personal credibility suggest firearm safe storage practices could feel pretty insulting. When you don't have credibility, say so, maybe like this:

> I imagine we both find it odd that someone like me, who has very little experience with firearms, would ask someone like you, who probably knows a lot about firearms, about any firearms you own and how you store them. If I were in your shoes, it might feel a bit like a fourteen-year-old questioning my right to have a license to drive. I raise the topic because I care about my patients, and I want us to be able to openly talk about how we can help you stay in the fight.
>
> Sometimes, when people are struggling with overwhelming stress in their lives, their firearms can become self-directed weapons. Many of my veteran patients have shared private thoughts that their loved ones would be better off without them, and this is the fundamental deception that drives self-destructive behavior.

> Far from being a gift, suicide causes massive collateral damage, deep and lasting devastation for families and loved ones. A suicide also puts a warrior's military brothers and sisters at greater risk for considering and acting on suicide themselves. Protecting the people you love from a tragic outcome doesn't necessarily mean removing your firearms. There are some creative ways to handle this kind of possible risk. Can we talk about those?

3. ***Who does the asking matters.***

If we have no personal credibility on a given topic, sometimes we can get help from those who already have credibility. One of the more innovative initiatives to roll out in the Department of Veterans Affairs was the hiring of veterans as peer support specialists. I worked closely with our clinic's peer support specialist as his primary mentor. We both offered different perspectives and skill sets to those we served. Sometimes, we sat together with the same patient, but most of the time, we coordinated care and tag teamed our approach, deploying complementary strengths.

There were times when I knew that I did not have sufficient trust with a particular veteran to ask questions about firearms. In these cases, he was a critical asset. He had the ability to boldly ask these questions of several veterans with minimal to no resistance on their part. He was able to negotiate things with them that would have been much more difficult for me. Having him ask the questions and negotiate safe solutions resulted in a better outcome and preserved the early trust I was building in some cases. It was a good example of how strengths can be magnified in a team, as they can be in the military.

4. ***Collaboration with those we serve leads to innovative solutions.***

Valuing lived experience is critical in this area, and the lack of actual collaboration is apparent because we continue to have conversations about the legalities of storing someone else's firearms during a time of potential crisis. If more people were talking with more veterans, first responders, and other firearm owners, they would be able to see that removal of a firearm is never necessary to protect firearm owners from suicide with their personally owned firearms.

I came to this conclusion myself during a critical moment in a session with one of my patients who freely acknowledged that he was at risk for turning his firearm into a weapon of self-destruction. He didn't want to die and was able to draw from the love of his beautiful daughters, who needed him to stay in the fight.

We had trust, honest conversation, and everything we needed to figure out a plan. He had asked me if I would temporarily hold on to his firearm, but this raised questions about the legalities and the ethics of doing so, not to mention the fact that we could not do this exchange anywhere near the VA campus, where the possession of any firearm could result in a felony charge for both of us. All of a sudden, he said, "Well, you know, if I just removed the firing pin, I wouldn't be able to fire it." Of course!

The firing pin is a tiny rod, usually less than two inches long, that must be present to engage the firing action. The firing pin can easily be removed when you break down a firearm to clean it. It is just a little piece of metal, not a weapon in and of itself. The same concept applies with the upper receiver on a rifle; it is just a piece of metal without which the firearm would not fire. That was the solution. I could hold his firing pin, and he could keep his firearm.

There would be no issues with bringing his firing pin to the VA. I could tuck his firing pin into an envelope and store it in my locked filing cabinet. Based on the trust we had, I knew he would not ask me to return it until he was out of the woods, so to speak. We were totally unified in our purpose to keep him in the fight for his daughters, if nothing else.

A few months later, another one of my patients was in the same situation, and we used the same solution. And weeks after that, another patient told me that he had given his firing pin to his mother during a time when he was in crisis. My veteran patients figured out an elegant solution because they have expertise with firearms. It's not a stretch for people who have cleaned their weapons hundreds of times to think about how a missing piece during reassembly will render their firearm inoperable.

Removing the firing pin can be a temporary arrangement, a safety measure warriors can use to stay in the fight during times of overwhelming stress. If more of us had meaningful collaboration with veterans, we might stop wasting time on questions that are not important — like the legalities of holding someone else's firearms — and start generating solutions like these, or other innovative, respectful solutions like the Warrior Box Project (www.docshaunaspringer.com) that is described in detail in a later chapter; further information is also included in the handbook.

QUESTIONS FOR REFLECTION AND APPLICATION

1. For many veterans, firearms become an extension of their identity. Are there any physical objects in your possession that are extensions of your identity? What personal qualities or sacred memories do these objects represent for you? How would it feel to you if someone were to question your ability to keep a highly valued personally owned object? How would you react if you thought they had the power to take it from you? What impact would such an interaction have on your willingness to open up and build trust with that person?

2. The idea that veterans see firearms as extensions of themselves is a dominant narrative that is true for many, but not all, veterans. Some veterans may never want to touch a firearm again after they are discharged from the military. Rather than making assumptions about what may be true for a given veteran, how can we approach conversations about firearms in ways that account for this possibility as well?

3. As we develop better approaches to conversations about firearm safety, it is critical for us to consider whether or not we have credibility in this area. Along these lines, when we know that we lack credibility on a given topic, we may experience a gut-level discomfort when having a conversation about it. What can we do with this feeling when it arises? To make application to your own growth, are you in the habit of disclosing the fact that you do not feel credible when this is the case? If not, why not? What do you fear would happen if you acknowledged a lack of credibility? What good things might happen if you could just admit this feeling?

4. When it comes to addressing risk factors for suicide, how can we discuss this in a way that conveys a caring, respectful attitude? What are some good indicators that a policy or practice is designed to protect someone other than the veteran or first responder, or other

individual that we are serving? In healing relationships, how can we balance support with risk-management concerns?

5. As we advance solutions to benefit particular groups of people, veterans, first responders, or others, are we fully collaborating with our end users? Is the way we collect data from them likely to elicit honest, open responses? If we agree that who is asking matters, how can we apply this insight to designing solutions where we live and work?

Don't forget to check out the handbook at the end of the book for further ways to apply this content.

5

SHAME ON YOU

A conversation about shame is really a conversation about moral injury. In contrast to the large body of research on effective treatment for post-traumatic stress, moral injury, which is a partially overlapping but discrete set of experiences, has received scant attention. As Litz and colleagues (2009) asserted, "There has been very little attention paid to lasting impact of moral conflict-colored psychological trauma among war veterans in the clinical science community ... serious exploration is indicated."[41]

In other words, the study of moral injury is in its infancy. Even the term "moral injury" is evolving. Based on my clinical expertise and review of the literature, in the current chapter, I will suggest a new framework for conceptualizing and treating moral injury. This new framework and the treatment approach that pairs with it will expand the current aperture of understanding, with the ultimate goal of advancing the field of study and practice, for all who have suffered from moral injuries.

The Moral Injury Concept

"Moral injury" was originally defined as the shame that results from participation in acts or events that violate someone's sense of morality. The classic examples are participation in atrocities of war or mistakes made in the fog of war. As an example, consider this excerpt from a letter written by a veteran who granted permission to share this on the TV program *Veterans Voices:*

> I saw you standing in the field alongside the road, and I aimed and fired. I felt no remorse at all at the time ... It all just boiled up in me, and I exploded. You represented the entire war to me. You had taken my friends who were genuinely trying to set your people free. You had robbed me of any remnant of clear morality or conscience. You had effectively imprisoned me and stolen any innocence or youth which might have remained.

Moral injury then evolved to mean not only the commission of acts deemed immoral to the self but also helplessness to act in ways that are aligned with personally held values. The classic examples in this case are helplessly witnessing the death of a battle buddy and helplessly witnessing the deaths of noncombatants, especially innocent children.[42] However, anchoring moral injury to acts of commission and omission misses the vast majority of shame-inducing experiences reported by the veterans I've worked with. Nor is shame always related to a discrete act or event.

One of the reasons it has been difficult to understand the scope of shame-based suffering is that warriors generally are a nondisclosing population. This is why I chose to open this book with the story of how my approach to practice has transformed over the past decade, from the time I entered the Department of Veterans Affairs as "Dr. Springer" and came to be known simply as "Doc Springer."

Creating a relationship of deep trust and mutual respect is critical if we are to truly understand the nature of how our strongest and bravest citizens may struggle. The very things that are most critical for us to understand as healers are the very things that are locked most deeply in the vault; these are the things that are *least* likely to be raised, even in settings where warriors are seen by highly trained clinical therapists.

Often the first story we hear is not the story we need to understand. The first story is actually quite often a test of whether we can be trusted, and whether we are capable of holding the kinds of deeper pain that are eating our warriors alive — the moral injuries that are more insidious, and often more lethal, than the anxiety part of post-traumatic stress that we have focused on so pointedly in the past few decades. The stories we need to be able to hear and the pain we need to support is exemplified in the story shared at the start of this chapter. That story was the "fox in the gut" that was eating that warrior alive as he lived and walked.

Expansion of the Moral Injury Concept

Based on the story behind the story that I've heard from many of my patients, there are a few surprising truths about the nature of moral injuries. The following observations can open the aperture of our understanding around moral injuries.

1. ***Surviving when loved ones (including brothers- and sisters-in-arms) have died can operate over time like a moral injury.***

   Just surviving when others we love don't can shift our entire moral framework for the rest of our lives. Consider the case of an Iraq War veteran who survived an IED (improvised explosive device) blast that killed his comrades. He may initially experience survivor guilt, asking himself why he survived when a brother- or sister-in-arms was killed. The initial survivor guilt he felt can harden over time into an all-consuming feeling of shame that he is unworthy and a burden who does not deserve to live when others "more deserving" have died.

   Here is how that often happens. Suppose that he experiences challenges during the transition out of the military, which is all too common. And actually, how could it be otherwise, when a person loses daily contact with their entire network of people they love like family?

Let's say that he has difficulty securing employment. Or it might be that his anxiety about the loss of structure and purpose in his life spills over into how he behaves with his loved ones. Let's say that on one particular day, his stress is overwhelming, and he loses his temper and yells at his six-year old daughter. Upon hearing the rage in his voice, his wife enters the room, and he sees a look of fear on the face of his wife and his daughter — the same facial expression he saw on the faces of an innocent Iraqi child and mother during a house-clearing mission.

He is suddenly filled with self-loathing, and in this state of mind, he compares himself to the ghost of his friend who died, stringing together a sequence of thoughts like this: "Warriors should protect the innocent. I have become a monster. My presence makes my family unsafe. Why was I chosen to live when someone that strong — a true warrior who never would have yelled at his kids — was killed in battle?"

This kind of narrative has been a theme in many of the stories of suicidal ideation among my patients. In fact, based on having worked with both military/first responder and civilian patient populations, I have repeatedly observed that the story of why our warriors die by suicide is often not the same as why civilians may die by suicide. I now believe that *shame* — as tied to *moral injuries* — is the overlooked link in the story of why we are losing our warriors to suicide.

2. ***Moral injury doesn't require that warriors do something outside of their moral code.***

In other words, we can be "morally injured" in a variety of scenarios that are beyond our control. For example, sexual assault is a moral injury in the deepest sense of the word. When someone sexually assaults another person, they are taking something that does not belong to them, in a way that can scar the soul of the person they have victimized. The person who has been injured may become infected by an overwhelming feeling of shame as they process the act of sexual violation, along with the helplessness and horror that a fellow human could have done this in the first place. This kind of shame often takes root in the core of our identity.

Interventions that attempt to highlight the victim's lack of culpability often do not stick. In other words, victims of assault can be well aware on the level of rational thought that being sexually violated is not their fault. They may nod their heads in agreement if a therapist makes this point. Yet, understanding and agreeing with the logic of this lack of culpability is a catch-22. If it's not their fault, then they have to reckon directly with the loss of power, the loss of control they might feel at the cellular level — which can be overwhelmingly terrifying.

In this way, the morally injurious impact of sexual trauma often stays deeply rooted after these kinds of interventions. Some people, out of the best of intentions, have said that "trauma is trauma," regardless of the source. However, based on two decades of work with survivors, it is clear to me that sexual assault is a particularly insidious form of moral injury. Why? Because sexual assault involves not only trauma-related feelings like helplessness and horror, but commonly, feelings of shame as well.

In my conversations with sexual assault survivors, a strong theme is that others ask them whether they "fought back." Some are able to fight back, but in many cases, their instinctive response is to freeze, rather than to directly challenge their attacker. Many are so shocked at the moment of the assault that they are unable to react in their own defense. Frequently, the "freeze" response is a form of tonic immobility that is controlled by involuntary body systems. Nonetheless, many survivors carry added shame based on their inability to defend themselves at the moment of the assault. When others ask them if they "fought back," if they were unable to respond at the time, this only increases their feelings of shame.

A second theme in survivor accounts is a cascade of further trauma and moral injury around reporting the assault. I am by no means the first person to make this point: when a survivor reports a sexual assault, others may react with disbelief or attempts to undermine their credibility. They may be twice victimized, when they are socially ostracized or punished by others. In the military context, maintaining a place of trust and belonging in one's unit is critically linked to a service member's emotional and mental well-being. Within this highly interdependent culture, social alienation from the unit becomes an acute risk factor for adverse outcomes, including depression, substance abuse and suicidal thinking. The "social punishment" or alienation that can occur after the report of a sexual assault conveys to an assault survivor that there is no safe place, and no safe person. (Fortunately, the presence of just one safe person, who believes the survivor, can make all the difference).

Another complicating factor is that sexual assault often leaves survivors with a feeling that they do not own — or control — their own bodies. The trauma symptoms can exacerbate this feeling of helplessness. For instance, quite commonly, survivors of sexual assault experience panic attacks. During panic attacks, they feel out of control when their bodies are flooded with adrenaline. This effectively mimics the original feeling of loss of control of their own bodies, which complicates recovery. If they do not receive trauma treatment that moves them to a place of recovery, this can leave trauma survivors with the feeling that they can never get past their trauma.

Another complicating factor is the process and outcomes related to justice seeking. Seeking justice requires individuals to share their story repeatedly, with first responders, with legal representatives, and as part of court testimony. The use, and misuse, of one's trauma story can result in even deeper moral injury. Collecting "medical evidence of assault" and accompanying disclosures can also be re-traumatizing for survivors.

Survivors take enormous risks in the hope of getting justice and preventing others from suffering. When these risks are met with a miscarriage of justice, the sense of helplessness survivors feel can be overwhelming. Furthermore, other public cases that remind them of their own experience (i.e., media coverage of major public figures on trial for sexual assault) are loaded with trauma triggers. Consider the concept of "a gift that keeps on giving" — this effect is just the opposite. This is a moral injury of the highest order — to be violated not once, but multiple times when you seek protection, support and justice.

3. ***Moral injury can be socially transmitted between groups of people.***

Socially transmitted shame can operate as a community-level moral injury. There are many examples of this: our treatment of Native Americans, people in the LGBT community, and people of color. Within my work with veterans, an example of this would be our society's treatment of Vietnam veterans. Specifically, in our behavior towards Vietnam veterans, we cast shame and blame on those who were deployed in support of the course of action that our leaders at the time decided to take.

Some of my patients reported that they were spit on or labeled in shameful ways ("baby killer" and so on). Others told me that even though those things never actually happened to them, and some even made a point to say that perhaps these practices were not as common as one might think, they may as well have occurred because Vietnam veterans were treated "like used toilet paper" when they came back from the war.

With a nation divided over the rightness and morality of the Vietnam War, those who answered the call to serve (including many who were drafted to serve) became scapegoats for our own unresolved shame around the war, and these veterans continue to bear the burden of this shame, which should not be theirs to carry. Vietnam veterans have frequently voiced the sense that they spent a year in hell and never made it back home.

In so many ways, the behavior of many Americans at that time communicated that our Vietnam veterans were no longer like us, were not welcome home, were not trusted or seen as assets but were seen instead as morally tainted by virtue of their service. Our Vietnam veterans have carried these cancerous feelings of shame and a disproportionate burden of grief *for decades.*

I have often wondered whether these things together help explain why nineteen out of the twenty veterans who die each day by suicide are *not* veterans of more recent wars in the Middle East, but are in fact veterans of earlier wars, where there is much unfinished business that I would classify as community-level moral injury.

4. ***Moral injury may be a part of what makes addiction so challenging to overcome, over and on top of physiological addiction.***

Can addiction be an act of moral injury that we commit habitually? Perhaps. Certainly, addictions are often paired with a feeling of shame. Addictions are also paired with increasing detachment from meaningful connection with others, and the sense of self that a person once knew. My practice in the area of addictions is relatively limited, so my goal is to propose that those who are more expert in this area might apply some of the lenses I share in this chapter to their own experiences.

5. ***Moral injury is not always related to a discrete act or event; it can accrue over time as a predictable set of moral traumas unfolds.***

   To give a common example, many Vietnam veterans made battle-field promises to look in on each other's family if they are killed in action. Sometimes these promises were paired with commitments to return a personal item of significance to the family (for example, a personal talisman or a family picture carried on the deceased). Despite promises made in full sincerity, they were often impossible to carry through.

   For example, without the internet or modern technology, finding people was much more difficult in the 1960s and 1970s. At other times, the overwhelming trauma of both the war and the return to a rejecting society prevented veterans from following through. What began with a feeling of guilt ("I never did what I promised Johnny I would do") calcified over decades into a feeling of deep personal shame ("I'm not loyal because I didn't honor my dying buddy's last wish").

   As I said previously, the same thing can happen with survivor's guilt: What began as guilt can harden into shame over time. Take the case of an Afghanistan War veteran who was riding in a convoy with her fellow soldiers when they were hit by an IED. She was injured while her buddies were killed. She was medically evacuated, suddenly pulled from the battle, and returned to the United States for treatment of her injuries.

   Even though she knows on a rational level that she was medically evacuated with potentially fatal injuries, she cannot kill the thought that she left her brothers and sisters behind in the warzone. She longs to return to the warzone. She feels guilty and helpless that she is recovering in the safety of a military hospital. This then becomes the metaphorical "fox in her gut": some combination of guilt for no longer being alongside her brothers and sisters in combat, overwhelming helplessness, rage at the loss of her fellow soldiers, a suddenly severed identity as a soldier, and a feeling of unworthiness to have survived when her peers were killed.

Understanding the difference between guilt and shame is key. Guilt is a feeling that you have done something that doesn't line up with your personal values. Guilt is not necessarily a bad thing in all cases; it has a useful function in correcting our behavior. If we do something that gives us that "sick stomach" guilt feeling, it should be a cue to examine our behavior and make a change.

Guilt doesn't mess with our internal self-concept in the same way that shame does. Shame penetrates much deeper than guilt and can make us feel unworthy, unlovable, and unredeemable. Guilt is about *what we have done,* and shame is about *who we are* as a person. Guilt is like a precancerous tumor that can turn into cancerous shame, which can metastasize throughout someone's entire being.

Based on these observations, I would suggest a reconceptualization as follows: Moral injury in the warrior[43] populations can be understood as a function of the space between an individual's personal warrior code and their self-perception. Here is an illustration to depict an expanded understanding of moral injury.

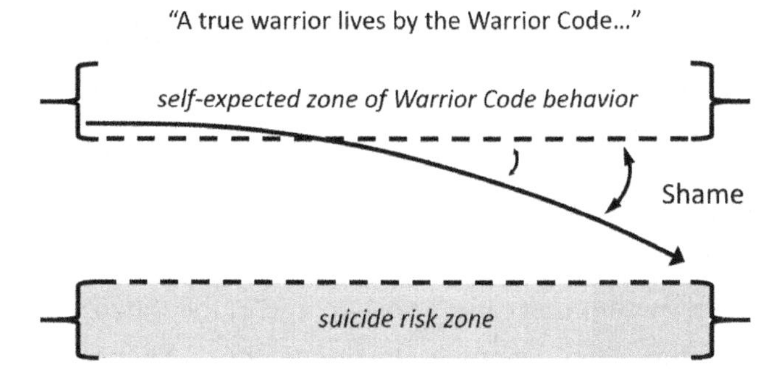

Often, shame that started as guilt can accrue over decades of time, not in relation to a single specific act, but instead based on things like the inability to uphold desirable behaviors, as in the case of a battlefield promise. Consider these excerpts from letters written by patients who attended a moral injury group I led at the VA. These show a common thread in stories of shame.

> "Your death left a hole in my heart and a guilt I cannot get rid of."

> "I tracked down your family. They were still grieving too. How do I put into words the regret and guilt of not reaching out for so many years?"

Reconceptualizing moral injury as the distance between service members' warrior code and their self-perception illuminates the story[44] that helps explain suicide within the military and first responder populations. In the general narrative across society, depression and hopelessness are thought to lead to suicidal ideation. Comparatively, among warriors, what I observed is that guilt and shame — not depression — was most closely linked to suicidal ideation. This is consistent with VA research which suggests that "for veterans with Post-Traumatic Stress, the strongest link to both suicide attempts and thinking about suicide is guilt related to combat."[45]

The story can be summarized in this way: When there is a divergence between service members' warrior code and their self-perception, there is shame. There is a pathway out of shame, which involves directly addressing the feelings of shame in the context of safe relationships with others who love and support us (see Chapter 7 for more on this).

When shame sits in our gut, it eats us alive, and it leads to a predictable set of behaviors — not just for warriors, but for all of us. People who feel ashamed may withdraw due to feelings of being unworthy of love, or alternatively, they may act out. Drinking and drugging is a form of acting out, an attempt to numb the painful feelings of shame. Likewise, explosive rage is a second example of acting out — and both are relationship-harming behaviors.

Relationship-harming behaviors and withdrawal invariably exacerbate shame. Take for instance the example of a person who behaves in ways that embarrass his family while he is drunk. Applying Thomas Joiner's Interpersonal-Psychological Theory of Suicidal Behavior[46] can help us see the factors that are closely linked to suicide risk. His theory has been tested through his ongoing research program and is a leading theory to predict suicidality. Here is an illustration of his model.

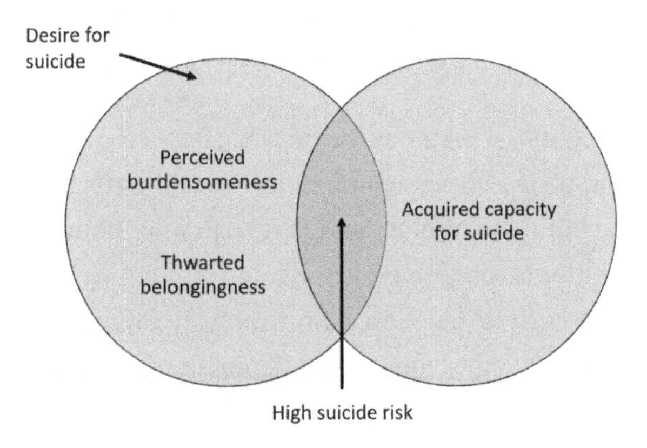

Joiner, T. *Why People Die by Suicide.* (Cambridge, MA: Harvard University Press, 2005).

Joiner's model suggests that those who have strong feelings of perceived burdensomeness and thwarted belongingness will have a heightened desire to die. Those with a heightened desire to die, who also have the acquired capacity to engage in self-directed acts of violence, will be at greatest risk for suicide. Joiner's theory was shaped in some part by his experience as a suicide loss survivor, the son of a Marine Corps veteran who died by suicide. Now let's bring the two models together, tracing the progression of shame to suicidality.

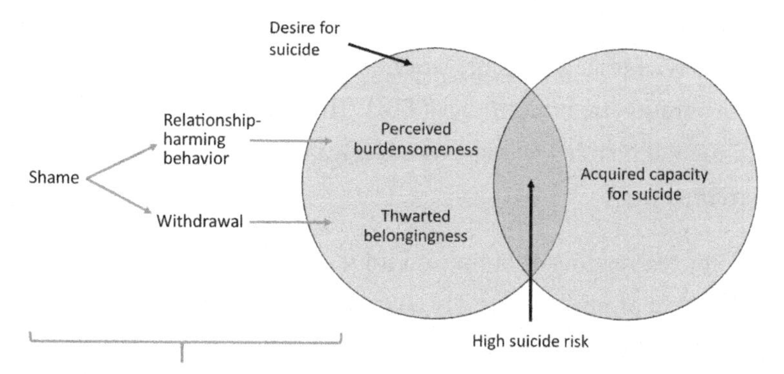

Mapping the contribution of shame onto Joiner's (2005) suicide risk model

As shown here, relationship-harming behaviors and withdrawal feed feelings of perceived burdensomeness and thwarted belongingness, which are often tied to suicidality. To return to the previous example, let's say that a person starts to see himself as a drunk who can't hold down a job to support his family (perceived burdensomeness). Or a person is horrified that he can't control the rage he directs at his young kids and begins to see himself as a threat to his family's safety.

Or take the case of a person who withdraws and sees herself as a person who will never fit in (thwarted belongingness). These are the examples of story lines that are integrally attached to the kind of cancerous shame that creates perceived burdensomeness and thwarted belongingness. And as Joiner articulates, because the training of warriors decreases factors that might inhibit self-directed violent behavior, they are more likely to take action on a desire to die.

My theory is that for military service members and first responders, a desire to die is less likely to be the result of depressed mood and more likely because they have been infected by the cancer of shame. I hypothesize that shame is the fox in their gut that is most closely related to suicidal ideation within the warrior populations.

Providers in the general mental health clinic where I worked for many years were assigned all of the patients who did not fit the diagnostic criteria for treatment in specialty clinics serving veterans with the most commonly recognized invisible wounds of war: post-traumatic stress (PTS) and traumatic brain injury (TBI). This effectively meant that, in general mental health, we had exceedingly large numbers of patients with diverse concerns.[47]

When I started reading about moral injury, I saw that this fit the experience of several of my patients. Heavily influenced by the pioneering work of psychiatrist Jonathan Shay, who observed that "the essential injuries in combat PTSD are moral and social and so the central treatment … actively encourages communalization of the trauma,"[48] I developed a group-based treatment to target these concerns. A detailed description of the protocol I used for these groups is beyond the scope of this book. However, the basic steps involved in these groups were as follows.

Moral Injury Group Model: Overview

Step 1: Provide a safe, mutually supportive group environment.

Step 2: Share the model for how treatment works (SAW model).

Step 3: Letter writing focused on perceived violations of each individual's warrior code, and the guilt and shame related to this.

Step 4: Letter reading and communal processing of shame-inducing experiences.

Step 5: Speak to the values that guide each group member's warrior code.

Step 6: Set a personal mission led by personally held warrior code values.

Step 7: Share post-traumatic growth gains with the group at long-term follow-up (three and six months later).

Step 1, creating a safe and supportive environment, is critical for every group therapy experience. This is core to the skill set of any licensed healer and should always be the first step in building the therapeutic container. Instructions on how to do this are well beyond the scope of this book, but there are many good books on effective practice. Some of my favorites are *The Heart and Soul of Change*[49] by Duncan, Miller, Wampold, and Hubble; and a number of books written by Dr. Irvin Yalom on effective group therapy, including *The Theory and Practice of Group Psychotherapy.*[50]

After creating a safe, supportive environment, Step 2 involves creating a metaphor that could be easily recognized and remembered by military service members. Many service members are familiar with a squad automatic weapon (SAW). For those who are not, I explain that a SAW is a very powerful, portable machine gun that sprays 556 rounds[51] with deadly force. A SAW is usually fitted with a bipod to support it while firing. We can use the acronym "SAW" to communicate that in cases of moral injury, feelings of shame, which often underlie suicidal behavior, are typically supported (maintained) by avoidance and withdrawal behaviors, as shown here.

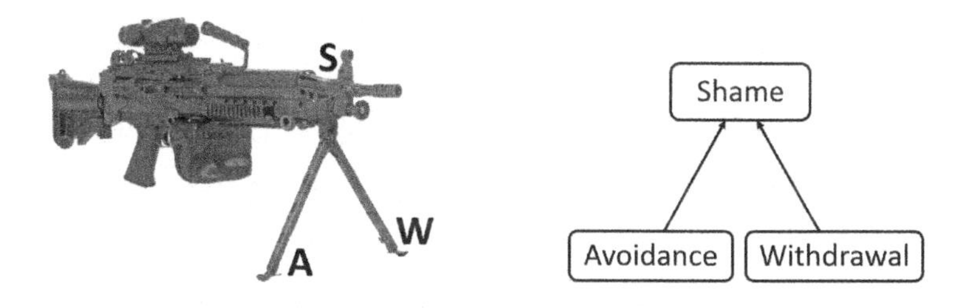

The use of this model is an example of how we can adapt our language to veteran culture, values and terminology. The pairing of the image of a powerful weapon with the feeling of shame communicates that shame is a formidable enemy. The use of the acronym SAW helped my veteran patients remember that shame is propped up by withdrawal and avoidance. Therefore, if we confront rather than avoid, and engage rather than withdraw, we will get traction in overcoming shame.

Step 3 involves letter writing, with a specific focus on perceived violations of each individual's warrior code, and the guilt and shame related to this.

Pennebaker[52] helped us understand how writing can be powerfully therapeutic for many people. Letter writing, by its very nature, is *relational;* when we write, we write *to someone.* Commonly, veterans in the group said that their letter took on a life of its own ("The letter talked back to me. It helped me remember things I had not thought about for years."). Or that it helped them remember long-forgotten experiences with great clarity ("Through the process of trauma letter writing, I realized something I had buried for forty years.").

To whom is a letter directed and what is the core content of each letter? Here there is flexibility. Every group member's letter is different. For example, one group member might write a letter to a fallen comrade, while another might write a letter to someone he killed, and another might write a letter to a younger version of herself. Similarly, the core content of the letter varies by group member. The therapist guides this process by helping each participant discern the shape of the particular fox in their gut and the best person to remove the fox.

Step 4 involves letter reading and communal processing of shame-inducing experiences. During this portion of the group, a full ninety-minute session is dedicated to each member's letter. The hardest letter to read is probably the one read by the first participant. At the same time, leadoff readers have also felt a sense of pride from having "walked point," or moved into territory that everyone is anxious about exploring.

Once the first letter has been read, an extremely powerful thing happens to the rest of the group: Based on the social norms in the group, it becomes countercultural for the other group members to take the easy path when others have done the hard thing. Because moral injury is relational in nature, communal processing becomes a very powerful strategy.

Next, during Step 5, each group member gives voice to the values that guide their personal warrior code. In my groups, participants often had several shared values — for instance, service to others, loyalty in relationships, and living with integrity or honor were common guiding values. In

Step 6, each group member defined and declared a personal mission led by his or her guiding values.

There was great flexibility in determining a personal mission. In some cases, this included meaningful connection with a leader associated with the spiritual or faith system of a particular patient. This mission was set flexibly, and in relation to each member's personal faith (if applicable). The role of faith leaders, chaplains, ministers, and spiritual healers was critical for some members of the group. To directly provide this was not my role, but to encourage and support this as a part of the healing process was critical for some of my patients.

It was inspiring to see the creativity and substance of character that group members brought to this process. Some group members decided to volunteer to serve other veterans or to work in animal shelters. Some took on a personal challenge such as doing a ruck[53] to raise awareness for an important cause.

Others defined a very specific mission to target the fox in their gut. For example, one veteran spent a substantial amount of time and money traveling to connect with family members of his fallen brothers. When he met the families, he shared stories of their loved ones, and together they visited their graves to honor their fallen loved ones.

Finally, Step 7 occurred at three and six months after the group finished. As a way to reassert their own warrior codes, group members had set a challenge for themselves — and the follow-up provided accountability. The follow-up meetings were especially enjoyable as group members formed a tribe again and shared stories of post-traumatic growth. A friendly competition was often observable; as in the military, they pushed each other to go further than each probably would have without this powerful form of social facilitation.

Group-based treatment using a peer support approach is highly effective for a few reasons. First, a person may or may not have an individual therapist that is a trusted doc. Even when someone is seeing a doc, it can still be hard to open up about feelings of shame in a one-on-one setting. However, shamed is canceled out in a group of peers who have had similar experiences. Once one person opens up, and that becomes the brave thing to do, others do the same.

Furthermore, in the letter reading part of the group, I have never, not once, witnessed anything other than a supportive response to an account of shame. Group members' capacity to embrace each other with compassion — no matter what the situation or how deep the shame — is consistently observable. As long as the letter reader approaches the task in a brave and honest way, the group can be counted on to express unqualified support. In this way, the group has a kind of moral authority to release the letter reader from the toxic burden of shame.

Second, effective treatment for moral injury restores
a person's understanding of their core values. To speak to your sacred values with a therapist is helpful. But to speak to the warrior code values that you share with other members of the group recreates the tribe. As I will explain in more detail in Chapter 9, it is the tribe, not a licensed professional acting as an army of one, no matter how much a doc is trusted, that ultimately has the greatest power to overcome the voice of despair. The tribe has lifesaving power. When we connect, we survive.

Finally, effective therapy requires people to take action on the values that drive a meaningful life. Setting a personal mission and saying it aloud to a group of peers provides a powerful way to redefine ourselves in community. It also provides accountability to take action. The follow-up sessions at three and six months out were important to holding the structure of the healing tribe and providing long-term accountability on the goals that were set.

Another strategic benefit of this moral injury group strategy is that it repositions the therapist in ways that are helpful for warriors. Instead of being saviors in a one-on-one healing relationship, therapists who run groups become extensions of the tribe that they help create. The tribe does the healing, and the therapist facilitates connection to what has the greatest power to heal moral injury. Recall the example of my patient who spent time and money traveling to join the families of his fallen brothers. The most effective part of the treatment happened when I, his therapist, wasn't even in the same zip code. This is what it looks like for a therapist to facilitate connection to a warrior's sacred values, rather than to try to be the hero of the story.

In taking action on their values, the patient restores a sense of personal honor. This may include repositioning themselves with the former "enemy" — those they may have seen as subhuman during a time of battle. In his book *What It Is Like to Go to War,* Karl Marlantes theorizes that the way to move past being visited by the ghosts of former combatants is to turn them into ancestors. As he explains, "remembering our common humanity and controlling the beast that wants to obliterate that memory is the task for all conscious warriors."[54] Other portions of the letter I presented at the start of this chapter read as follows:

> I remember now [what happened], and I am so very, very sorry. You might have had a family … a wife … children … How did they find out what had happened? Were you a soldier like me … Did your comrades find you and pledge vengeance? … I want you to know that I only came over there to help. I think of you often. I pray that your family has some peace. In some ways, you guide me … I try to be a good man, loving all nations. My God has forgiven me, and what I need now is to forgive myself.

Some of the questions I asked on the expanded measure of post-traumatic stress that I described in Chapter 3 touched on moral injury. For example, after completing this group, there were decreases on how much my patients endorsed items like "Feeling like an empty shell inside." Similarly, their avoidance of others decreased, and their capacity to have warm, loving feelings increased. One of the most fascinating things I observed was a change in the way they responded to the question, "Seeing or hearing things others don't (i.e., enemy combatants that appear real) even though you know what you are seeing isn't real."

I created this question because my nonpsychotic patients kept telling me about hearing or seeing things that were remnants of their war experiences. For instance, many had flashes of enemy combatants during waking hours or felt a strong presence of an enemy combatant standing in their room at midnight. Some heard voices whispering, in the language of the enemy (e.g., voices whispering in Farsi). It wasn't true psychosis because they were consistently aware that these odd perceptual experiences were not actually happening in real life.

Awkwardly worded though my question was, I tracked this particular item in a subsample of combat warriors to see how common it is for them to have these experiences. In a sample of thirty-six combat veterans, half of them (eighteen of thirty-six) reported having these kinds of striking perceptual experiences. As my understanding of guilt and shame has unfolded, I now wonder if my question captured the experience of being haunted by ghosts that are tethered by feelings of guilt or shame, because when the group did its work, this symptom — and perhaps the ghosts — also faded.

UNIVERSAL PRINCIPLES I LEARNED FROM WORKING WITH WARRIORS

1. ***Guilt and shame are not the same thing, but guilt can become shame over time.***

   Whereas guilt arises in relation to behaviors that are not in line with our personal values, shame goes much deeper; shame is about who we are as a person. Even though these experiences are not the same thing, guilt may be transformed into shame over time when a person feels helpless to correct whatever is inducing feelings of guilt.

2. ***Feelings of guilt and shame are not always related to a discrete act or event.***

   Just as trauma is not always related to a discrete event,[55] guilt and shame do not always arise in relation to acts or events. A more helpful framework for understanding both guilt and shame is that both are a function of the misalignment between the values we hold for our ideal selves and our private self-perception.

3. ***The "story of suicide" for warriors (and potentially for many others in society as well) may have less to do with depression and more to do with a metaphorically cancerous form of shame.***

   While depression may shape the story of suicide for many in our society, shame figures prominently as a cause for suicide within the population of warriors. Since shame is not a formal diagnosis (and neither, as yet, is moral injury for that matter), many who suffer may never have touchpoints with mental health treatment. In fact, recent CDC data[56] suggests that 50% of those who have died by suicide have not had a mental health diagnosis. This makes it critical for all of us, as a society, to learn to recognize and address the accumulation of guilt and shame that can lead to suicidal intentions.

4. ***Groups of peers have extraordinary power to help address guilt and shame.***

   Groups provide social facilitation and accountability for realigning behaviors with one's core values. This is true for all kinds of groups that support life changes. In addition, groups have the power to become a moral authority that can address the cancerous effects of shame. Based on my clinical observations, I suspect that future research will demonstrate that group-based treatment for moral injury is the most effective form of treatment.

QUESTIONS FOR REFLECTION AND APPLICATION

1. Many of my veteran patients struggled with moral injuries, a challenge that is different from post-traumatic stress. Had you ever heard of the term "moral injury" before reading this chapter? Have you ever experienced moral injuries in your own life? Have they always been the result of discrete acts or events, or have some of them resulted from chronic situations that you were helpless to control?

2. I observed a conversion of guilt into shame over time within some of my patients, even when they agreed that a damaging situation had been out of their control. Do you agree or disagree with the idea that guilt can become shame over time? How does your personal experience and your observation of others' experiences inform your understanding of this?

3. Warriors often live by a warrior code. There are advantages to living by a set of values and standards. Could there also be some unique vulnerabilities associated with holding these standards? When do we need to extend compassion to ourselves during times when we miss the mark, for example, during times of transition, stress, moral injury? How can we do this without losing the good things about upholding standards for our choices and behaviors?

4. As you consider the concept of a warrior code, when you take stock of your own life, in what ways is your experience noticeably out of alignment with your values and personal ideals? Can you set a challenge for yourself to realign something that needs attention?

5. Once I developed trust with my patients, I began to see that their hidden pain was eating them alive, like the fox in the gut of the boy of Sparta mentioned in the introduction to this book. In your own life, is there any unresolved trauma that operates like a fox in your

gut? If so, could writing a letter help you get clarity on how to move towards healing? A letter need not be sent. Writing unsent letters can be a very effective way to process painful emotional experiences.

Don't forget to check the handbook at the end of the book for further ways to apply this content.

6

FOXES

I'll always remember the time I was called in to intervene with a veteran who was actively threatening to set off a bomb in the VA. He initially presented as rageful at the VA and everyone who works in the VA. When I got into the room with him, he told me that he wanted to die and to take us all with him. I sat with him until his rage dissipated, at which point he started to cry and revealed the fox that was in his gut.

He told me that he felt broken and alone ever since his wife of twenty-five years had passed away from cancer. Then he told me that she was the only one he could talk to and that this was the anniversary of her death. He wept deeply while we sat, side by side, on the floor of the urgent care exam room, with our backs against the wall. When the wave of grief had passed, he smiled, his face transformed in some indescribable way. It's hard to put into words other than to say that I saw the light of hope return to him in that moment.

Grief is another form of hidden pain that many in our society — including our warriors — are carrying. It is like shame in a couple of interesting ways. When the full force of either emotion hits us[57] all at once, it can greatly escalate the risk of self-destructive behavior. Second, both can accrue slowly and steadily over many years, hollowing us out over time. You could fill a book with what I have learned about grief since I started working at the Tragedy Assistance Program for Survivors (TAPS). Perhaps someday I will, in collaboration with my colleagues at

TAPS. The scope of the current book is to share only what I learned prior to coming to TAPS.

Acute Grief Can Be Dangerous

All other things being equal, the times when I was most worried about losing my patients to suicide was when they had suffered the recent loss of a fellow veteran. Sometimes they lost battle buddies in combat. Death is a fact of war, but accepting this does not lessen the impact of grief. An anthropologist named David Marlowe studied the comparative impact of combat traumas — specifically, killing an enemy soldier, witnessing a violent death, and having a friend die.

Sebastian Junger highlighted these findings in his book *Tribe*: "In war after war, Army after Army, losing a buddy is considered the most devastating thing that could possibly happen."[58] After losing a battle buddy to combat, my veteran patients were gripped by a sense of helplessness, covered by rage. They wanted to be back in the combat zone. They often expressed that if they had been there, maybe this might not have happened. They wondered aloud whether they could have spotted the enemy's IED or if they could have been killed in their brother's place, an outcome some voiced as preferable to the pain of the loss.

Understandably, many wanted to take revenge on the enemy who had killed their brother- or sister-in-arms. For example, one of my patients, a combat medic, was asked to treat an enemy combatant who had been shot in the neck, paralyzed but still alive. While treating this enemy soldier, he found the dog tags of one of his comrades around his enemy's neck. He instantly turned his weapon on the enemy soldier, firing repeatedly until he ran out of ammo. As he reflected back on this, he said, "If he was here now, I'd tell him I'm sorry he died that day because I want to kill him all over again."

Those who had already been struggling with survivor's guilt were often the most impacted by combat losses. Even among those who were medevaced out with terrible injuries, there was often a sense of guilt about not being there with their unit, and a self-directed rage borne of helpless frustration. As psychiatrist Jonathan Shay has pointed out, "self-blame seems almost universal after the death of a special comrade, regardless of the presence or absence of the 'real' basis for it … grief and guilt often seem to merge in the wake of a close friend's death in battle."[59] To decrease the risk of self-destructive thoughts and behaviors, therapy needed to be a safe space for exploring all of this so that this guilt would not turn into the kind of shame that may lead to suicidal thoughts.

Compared to combat deaths, losses to suicide were even more dangerous. During my time at the VA, a veteran who was beloved within the local community of veterans died by suicide. He left the following note: "It's not anyone's fault. I just wasn't strong enough to fight my demons anymore." His death rocked the entire community of veterans. His suicide was the focus of many therapy sessions in the weeks following his death. Those sessions had particularly high stakes. The mix of emotions in the room was a toxic compound of helpless rage, helplessness, paralyzing fear, hopelessness, and soul-searing grief.

Most of the time, as in this case, the suicide of a fellow veteran has not been anticipated by friends and family. In fact, many times an individual who dies by suicide had appeared to others to be high functioning, perhaps even a leader among his or her peers, prior to the death. To normalize the effect of these sudden traumatic losses for my patients, I developed the concept of the "sniper effect." The naming of it as the sniper effect was helpful to my patients because it accurately captured the feeling of losing a fellow veteran to suicide: They had suddenly lost someone to an unknown, unseen enemy. In the context of what turned out to be a mostly private battle, the demons[60] of their fallen brother or sister seemed to suddenly ambush them.

In cases of suicide loss, the rage was palpable. Rather than being directed at a flesh-and-blood force of enemy combatants, however, the rage had no single clear target. Sometimes, the rage was directed outward in one of several possible ways. Often, blame was attributed to the failure of the system of care to adequately support their friend. For example, a common theme was expressed that their friend tried to get help but all they did was throw pills at him or force him to fill out a stack of forms before he could see someone, so he dropped out of treatment. Less commonly, but not infrequently, the rage was directed at the military for a perceived failure in leadership within a given chain of command. At times, God was blamed. Or the target of blame was the veteran's family, perhaps a partner or a spouse.

Sometimes the death was felt as a personal betrayal, and the rage was directed at the person who died. In these instances, their friend's choice to die by suicide was seen as violating the sacred trust upon which their relationship had been built. Reasoning that they had fought a war together, literally trusting each other with their lives, they wondered why that trust had failed at their friend's time of need? Why did their battle buddy not tell them that he felt hopelessly overmatched by his demons? In response to the suicide of a battle buddy, the deepest cry of many of my patients was this: "Why didn't he understand that if he had just told me what was going on, I would have dropped everything and gotten on the next flight to come to him? Why didn't he *trust me enough* to give me that chance?"

Sometimes, rather than directing the rage at their buddy, the rage was instead directed at themselves. This showed up in a shame-inducing string of toxic thoughts, as in "What does this say about me that she could not tell me how much she was struggling?" or "How could I have missed the signs of his pain? He was closer to me than my own family, and yet I never noticed that he was suffering." In cases where rage was directed inward, there was an overwhelming sense of helplessness.

In addition to rage, there was often fear. The fear they expressed reminded me of the fear people sometimes express when their healthy, young friend dies suddenly of a heart attack. Because their friend's battle was often privately waged, and they had not predicted the suicide, they wondered if they themselves could suddenly become suicidal. Could they catch the wish to die by suicide and leave their own family bereft? Could they fall prey to their own demons at some point, and be taken out by the same silent sniper that took their friend's life? This fear was especially strong when the warrior who died was perceived to be a leader among his peers. If the fear had a voice, it would say something like: "He was so strong, and yet he died by suicide, so what does that say about my chances?"

In some cases, rather than feeling fear, which implies a desire to avoid dying by suicide oneself, the suicide was seen as the expected outcome of a private battle with demons. The risk of self-destructive thoughts was particularly high when the loss was received in this way. Often this interpretation of the death signaled that my patient identified with their buddy because they had been privately losing traction in a similar battle.

For people who are already on the ropes against their demons, suicide can seem like a more viable option for ending pain when their battle buddy has chosen suicide. People at the end of the tunnel of despair feel fairly detached from others. They literally have tunnel vision at the time of greatest risk. They are often unable to see with clarity that suicide causes massive collateral damage and leaves a wake of endless devastation for their loved ones. At the end of the tunnel, pain crowds out almost everything else.

Attachment, Trust, and Grief

Attachment theory can help us understand the link between suicide risk and the loss of fellow warriors. My first job in psychology, which involved the study of attachment theory and research, has influenced my thinking ever since. A quick review for those who may be less familiar: Attachment is initially formed in childhood, and it is continually shaped throughout our lives by the people and events we encounter.

Attachment is about *trust* — trust that the world is a basically safe place, trust that others will respond supportively to our needs, and trust in our own capacity to successfully navigate our relationships and the world around us. Children who develop secure attachment feel confident that their needs will be met. Therefore, they ask directly for what they need.

The ability to ask directly for what we need is a hallmark of secure attachment; it is the behavioral pattern of those who stand without armor, confident in the love of their tribe. Those who develop insecure attachment have some doubt about others' ability or willingness to respond to their needs. Insecure attachment styles may develop in families where parental attention is inconsistent or largely absent.

In fact, children who have suffered physical or emotional abuse, or pervasive neglect, may develop an avoidant attachment style. Those who become avoidantly attached have learned not to trust anyone to meet their needs. They are consistently reluctant to trust others, preferring instead to rely on themselves. So, the term "avoidant attachment" is a contradiction, really. We might as well see "avoidantly attached" people as detached from others, rather than attached.

When you begin to see the experience of grief through the lens of attachment, further insights arise. If the power of attachment has a force that is greater than the power of despair (which I will fully unpack in Chapter 9), then it follows that the loss of an attachment could directly induce feelings of despair. Why is the suicide rate so much higher after discharge from the military? There are many reasons, but I think that one major factor is that service members lose the tribe that has become their family.

My theory is that for many service members, the military experience fundamentally reconstitutes their attachment system. For those who grew up in chaotic or unsupportive backgrounds who enter a healthy military unit, that unit may become the family they never had. Discharge, then, is a forced cutoff from their reconstituted attachment system, an attachment wound of the highest order.

In many cases, service members may be dealing with grief upon grief upon grief when they discharge and thereafter — reflecting on those taken from them in battle, the loss of closeness with their military family, and the helplessness of seeing their brothers and sisters fall prey to their demons. Those with weak attachment bonds in their biological families who find family with their military brothers and sisters may feel *orphaned* after discharge. Some may feel marooned in a society whose individualistic values oppose collectivist military values.

Interactions with civilians who display an ignorant approach to veterans issues, who may ask intrusive questions, and who demonstrate a mind-boggling tendency to focus on shallow matters and to idolize shallow people, may become pervasive, constant triggers, reminding them of what they feel is now missing in their lives. The fear, social rejection, and hero worship from civilians further alienates them from meaningful connection and makes them feel inclined towards avoidant attachment (that is to say, detachment) from society.

In the final analysis, trauma alone may not be the thing that catalyzes despair. Instead, it may be the combination of trauma, grief, survivor guilt, and the gaping attachment wounds that service members feel when they separate from the tribe that had their back during their time in service.

Connecting this to attachment theory also helps us see why suicide loss is so much more dangerous than other types of loss. Why? Because the nature of the loss can make us question the strength of the attachment we have had with the deceased. For my veteran patients, it can rock their trust in a person that may have literally been a lifeline to them in the past. It may challenge a life-preserving feeling that what they had in combat was *real* and can be relied upon *in all battles.*

The love and trust between veterans *is real,* and suicide is multicausal, but my theory is that the contagion of suicide risk between veterans has a lot to do with the way that suicide undermines secure attachment. Among my patients, those who lost a battle buddy to suicide doubted whether they really knew their friend. They doubted whether their friend really trusted them, and they approached their future with a new fear that they might lose more friends, or possibly their own desire to stay in the fight.

Grief Is Often Camouflaged

Suicide awareness campaigns have indeed raised awareness — perhaps to a fault. You would be hard pressed to find an American citizen nowadays who has never heard the statistic that twenty veterans a day die by suicide. With all of the "veteran suicide awareness" campaigns, sometimes I wonder if we have crossed the line into numbness. Despite having some awareness of the scope of the problem, for most civilian Americans, there is no direct connection to the actual suffering of those closest to the veterans who die.

Many veterans are survivors of suicide, even though they will never identify as such, and we are missing the boat by a nautical mile in this area. If twenty veterans a day die by suicide,[61] then it logically follows that many veterans are suicide loss survivors, often several times over. In fact, Cerel and colleagues sampled 812 lifetime suicide-exposed individuals and estimated that for each suicide, 135 people were personally exposed (i.e., knew the person).[62] Since these estimates were based on the general population rather than veterans, who have been embedded in interdependent military units, this number is probably even greater for veterans.

Mattis and Schake describe a "grief gap" in their book, *Warriors and Citizens: American Views of the Military.* As they explain, "the public is largely unaffected by deaths and wounds from the wars, and we have few public rituals beyond Veterans Day and Memorial Day to involve the public and pull the military into the broader society in times of grief … what had been a more common experience of loss in previous wars now tends to be an isolating experience for military families."[63]

I echo the concerns of Mattis and Schake: psychologically speaking, abstract awareness of a problem without a personal emotional connection to the pain of those affected by it can contribute to apathy when it comes to investing the time and money required to effectively address the problem. We do more talking about warriors than walking with them.

Not only is grief overlooked in the public conversation, but it is also largely overlooked in clinical spaces where warriors are served as well. Several factors account for this. First, clinical providers learn about what they assess. Those who treat veterans routinely ask about symptoms of anxiety, depression, suicidality, addictions, and injuries related to blast exposures. Grief and loss is just not a focus. Neither is it part of the core curriculum in most psychology graduate schools, nor a focus of post-graduate training, even in settings where military service members and first responders are served. To further compound this gap in our knowledge, there are also several reasons why those who suffer are unlikely to raise the topic of grief and loss.

Sometimes, guilt and shame about how their fallen service member died locks their grief away. In other cases, veterans may be numb to their pain, and they themselves may see their grief as an expected part of military service that is not deserving of the focused attention of a treatment provider. Patients may see the role of "talk docs" as being limited to the treatment of mental health conditions like post-traumatic stress, depression, and addictions. For some, grief may fall into a separate, more ambiguous category of human suffering, one that may feel very private for those who suffer.

In fact, there can be a feeling of disloyalty that arises for some veterans when they consider talking about the loss of battle buddies. This is because grief is often intertwined with the love they have for their brothers- and sisters-in-arms. Some of my patients have disclosed an initial fear that my goal as a treatment provider might be to help them process their grief so that they can "get over it" and "move on" — a reasonable fear as the goal of trauma-focused therapies is to help people process and thereby lessen the intensity of trauma memories.

Those who grieve don't want to move on because the pain of their grief keeps them connected to their fallen brothers. Having people process grief so they can get over it is actually the polar opposite of healthy grieving, but this fear moves some who suffer to lock their grief in the vault.

Healthy Grieving

What can we do to support our warriors, who are shouldering such burdens of grief, and others in our lives who are suffering the loss of loved ones? Again, attachment theory offers us an ideal framework for understanding how to support those who are grieving.

When a person is hit by a sudden loss, from an attachment perspective, they are often highly susceptible to attachment wounds during the overwhelmingly painful time period that follows. Attachment wounds can occur when we perceive that we cannot depend on others to support us at a time of need. Assuming others are aware of a loss, it's common for our friends and family to reach out in a burst of support in a time of crisis. They may show up for the memorial, write cards, and bring us meals. But then, after a few weeks or months, they go back to focusing on other things.

If we reflect on this phenomenon, what I call the "burst of support effect," we can see that it applies across a variety of life-changing events. When there's a health crisis, like a cancer diagnosis or a debilitating car accident, or even a happy event like the birth of a baby or a wedding, friends' and neighbors' support usually is limited to a period of a few weeks or months. So, the burst of support effect is a common, socially normed way to respond to the needs of others. Therefore, it's important to realize that it's not personal. When people withdraw their attention to our needs, it doesn't mean that they don't care.

While we can do our best to remember we're loved, the burst of support effect is still problematic when the most urgent needs of those who are grieving come well after the loss. Immediately following a loss, surviving loved ones may be in a state of shock and experiencing feelings of disorientation and numbness. Once the initial shock wears off, waves of grief may hit, inflicting sharp and sudden pain. Just as the burst of support effect is nearly universal, the delayed impact of trauma is common.

So, one of the ways we can help those who are grieving is to anticipate the burst of support effect, and offer stable and secure attachment in response to loss. This requires intentionality on our part. For example, one very practical way to support others is to put a reminder in our phones to regularly check in and see how things are going. When we do call, the best way to support is just to listen and hold safe space for those who are grieving to feel whatever they are feeling.

Second, we can help those who are grieving hold their attachment with a loved one who died. Healthy grieving does not mean putting a loved one out of one's mind. Instead, the goal of healthy grieving is to help people connect with the loved one in new ways, to integrate and honor what is sacred, and to hold that connection. Drawing again on an attachment perspective, healthy grieving can be reconceptualized as the continuation of secure attachment.

Clarifying the goal of grief work can help us engage our nation's warriors in treatment and better support them outside of formal healing roles. We can give them very clear assurance that there is nothing treatment can do to remove any of the experiences that they hold sacred. We can tell them that our goal is to support continued connection and enhance positive memories of a loved one who has died. We can do this by saying their loved one's name, listening to stories about their loved one (including the hilarious ones), and bearing witness to the importance of the relationship they have. We can also help them find personalized ways to approach and sit with their grief.

We can help them renew and restore their relationship with someone they have lost. In many cases, especially in the case of suicide, a death is associated with a break in secure attachment in the relationship. When those who are grieving feel safe with us, we can help them work through this kind of pain. For instance, I have often asked my veteran patients what they would do if the person they lost were to walk into the room. Both the complicated emotions that arise and the need to restore connection shows up very clearly in their responses. As one patient said, "I would punch him in the face. Then I would give him a big hug."

Finally, we can support those around us by rounding out our education of this critical topic. What we do to address the needs of loss survivors to reduce the risk of further losses by suicide can and should be migrated to how we support warriors who have lost battle buddies. Tragedy Assistance Program for Survivors leads the field in supporting those grieving the loss of a military loved one. Since 1994, TAPS has provided care to families of the fallen, serving over seventy-five thousand individuals.

In the past decade, under the leadership of TAPS vice president Kim Ruocco, TAPS has developed specific programming for suicide loss (what is called "postvention"), in recognition of the unique needs of suicide loss survivors. My colleagues at TAPS draw from both their lived experience and their professional expertise to help advance postvention practices.

During my time as senior director of Suicide Prevention and Postvention Initiatives at TAPS, I helped launch a series of innovative trainings on grief and loss, and TAPS best practice postvention model. Here are examples of trainings that are available online free of charge, thanks to generous sponsorship from the Boeing Foundation and the NFL Foundation.

- Postvention: Healing After Suicide Loss
- Understanding Why People Die by Suicide
- Grief and Trauma: Making Critical Distinctions and Planning Treatment
- Grief to Growth: A Roadmap to a Healthy Grief Journey

- Stabilizing Military Units After Suicide Loss
- Stabilizing Families After Suicide Loss
- Intimate Partners and Suicide Loss
- Treating Grief in the Veteran Population
- Post-Traumatic Growth After Suicide Loss

UNIVERSAL PRINCIPLES I LEARNED FROM WORKING WITH WARRIORS

1. ***Suicide loss exposure can directly increase the risk of suicide for those impacted.***

   "Postvention" refers to the care of those who have been impacted by suicide loss. When I was at the VA, I repeatedly observed the impact of suicide loss on my patients in the ways I have described, but at the time, I didn't know the term "postvention." I didn't have a coherent model for how to support suicide loss survivors in a research and theory-informed way at that time.

   Tragedy Assistance Program for Survivors (TAPS) has led the field for many years in developing best practice postvention strategies. The TAPS postvention model has been refined over more than a decade in a group of more than twelve thousand suicide loss survivors. This is the field-leading model for supporting those who are impacted by suicide loss. Learn more at their website (www.TAPS.org/suicide).

2. ***People often hide their grief, even in places where it is supposed to be safe to address human struggles.***

   For many reasons, as described earlier in this chapter, veterans and other people may conceal their grief experiences. As a society, we often avoid grief, and we do not have a clear model for how to support those who are grieving. The grief gap is a substantial problem, not only where veterans are served, but also in many of the places where people come to address their suffering. Being clear that our intent is not to urge people to get over it and move on can help people who are grieving feel safer to describe their grief. It is worth repeating that in my experience, often the best way to support others is just to listen and hold safe space for those who are grieving to feel whatever they are feeling.

3. ***The burst of support effect is a common phenomenon for all kinds of losses.***

   The burst of support effect is not personal. It's commonly observed across many situations. However, it is problematic nonetheless because support is often withdrawn at the very time when those who are grieving need increased support. Since our default mode is to support others for a relatively brief period of time, it requires intentionality to change our behavior in this area.

4. ***Healthy grieving is about restoring attachment to a loved one who has died.***

   When people lose someone, grief helps them find that person again. Sometimes, there are issues in the relationship that need to be addressed before a healthy attachment can be restored. Finding ways to reconnect and carry that love forward is the way to heal from loss.

   This is so important that I developed a specific exercise entitled "Reconnecting with a Fallen Battle Buddy" to support this practice. I developed this exercise to help veterans carry forward the love they have for their fallen brothers- and sisters-in-arms. It can be modified to help any of us reconnect with loved ones that we have lost. This exercise can be found in the handbook portion of this book and may be photocopied and used without limit as long as authorship attribution is made.

QUESTIONS FOR REFLECTION AND APPLICATION

1. Many of our nation's warriors are survivors of suicide loss, even if they might not identify themselves in this way. Have you been personally impacted by suicide loss? What emotions or thoughts have come up for you in relation to that loss? Can you identify with any of the experiences described by my patients?

2. To what degree have you been aware of the burden of grief that is shouldered by those serving in our military? If you have any military loved ones, how can you be a safe, stable person to support their grief?

3. Many of my veteran patients were initially reluctant to disclose their grief. To what degree do you tell others you trust about your own experiences of grief? Do you share it or lock it down? If you lock it down, what prompts you to do so?

4. In this chapter, I described the burst of support effect as a commonly observed pattern in how we, as a society, respond to others' grief. Have you ever personally experienced the burst of support effect after a loss in your life? How did you make sense of it at the time? What does this experience lead you to do for others in your life who may be suffering? Is there anyone else in your life right now, veteran, first responder, or otherwise, whom you can make an intentional commitment to support in an ongoing way?

5. Healthy grief allows us to continue our relationship with a loved one who has died. However, sometimes, as in the case of the example I shared in this chapter, there may be mixed feelings and unfinished business. If you have lost someone in your life, how is your relationship with them now? If they were here, what would you say to them or how would you interact with them? In what ways can you continue

to keep the connection with them alive in the ways you live your life? Based on these insights, how can you support those who are suffering from grief?

Don't forget to check the handbook for further ways to apply this content.

7

A WARRIOR WITHOUT ARMOR

"Honestly, Doc, I would rather walk into the kill zone of an ambush than tell my wife how much I need her." When a special forces operator looks straight at you with a face full of fear and dread, it gets your attention. That is how Joe (not his real name) looked at me in the middle of a therapy session. I had just shared some counsel on how to repair his badly strained marriage.

During the first few therapy sessions, Joe presented as someone with a serious anger management problem. He enjoyed fighting and felt a sense of release after physical conflicts. He was spoiling for a fight, coiled up and hoping someone would provoke him to violence. He scored high on some of the supplemental prompts I asked in my assessments, like "Missing the adrenaline rush of combat and frequently wishing you were back in the combat zone" and "Wishing someone would pick a physical fight with you because it would feel good to fight." The first story he told me to explain his anger was that people who haven't served have no respect for the military. Joe's personal mission was to "reeducate the ignorant" by way of knuckle sandwiches.

As we built trust, though, another story emerged. Joe had always been particularly close to his wife. He described her as his rock. In attachment terms, this means that she was the "stable base" who created his sense of security as he went through life. After his last deployment, their marriage had become seriously strained. In one session, he told me that he had tried reaching out to his wife, but she had walked away. Joe said, "It felt like I was reaching my arms out to her, and she just cut them off and let me bleed out."

In attachment terms, by turning away from him at a time of vulnerability and need, his wife was effectively saying "You're dead to me." This was setting off what master therapist Sue Johnson refers to as a "primal panic." As Johnson, the founder of emotionally focused therapy, explains:

> Our loved one is our shelter in life. When this person is unavailable and unresponsive, we are assailed by a tsunami of emotions — sadness, anger, hurt and above all, fear. This fear is wired in. Being able to rely on a loved one, to know that he or she will answer our call is our innate survival code. Research is clear, when we sense that a primary love relationship is threatened, we go into a primal panic.[64]

While Joe had sufficient restraint not to take his anger out on his wife, he was taking it out on a growing number of other people. Frankly, the situation was quickly becoming very dangerous. In this case, the work involved coaching him in how to address the loss of trust and intimacy in his marriage. This was what caused him to look at me with such fear and dread. Clearly, repairing his relationship called for a different kind of courage than the kind required to operate in the combat zone. But Joe dug deep and took the risk of standing before her, without armor, in the way that I had suggested.

Joe's wife then responded by taking a risk and opening up to him in return. She shared that while he was deployed, she found a letter confirming that he had volunteered to redeploy. With young twin boys still in diapers, they were due to have a third child, and he had told her that he had no choice but to return to combat. She explained that when she found the letter, she felt like he had abandoned her and their children. She nursed her rage during the time he was away and she was alone with their two toddlers and a newborn.

So, there were two layers of stories behind the original story he initially told me. Both Joe and his wife were suffering because of the attachment wounds they had inflicted on each other. If I had failed to learn these truths, and treated this as a standard anger management case, the outcome would have been very different — for Joe and whomever he would have targeted, driven as he was by his hidden pain.

Once the foxes in their guts were revealed, Joe and his wife were able to ask each other for forgiveness and to reestablish trust and intimacy. He looked like a different person at our next session. In that indescribable way I can't quite put into words, his face changed. He looked happy and hopeful, and there was no recurrence of any violent behavior towards anyone after he and his wife reestablished their bond.

At the end of therapy, Joe gave me a gift — something you could probably buy for less than a few dollars, but it is among the most precious gifts I've ever received. He gave me a parachute cord with this explanation: "Once, when I was on a training mission, my parachute didn't open. This cord was the backup. It was the one that needed to work, or I probably would have died. This cord saved my life."

Joe was one of my earliest treatment cases at the VA. He helped me see that courage takes different forms. He started me on a path to thinking about attachments in the context of military families, how people build trust, and what it takes to make someone a part of our tribe. Another formative experience occurred when I observed the frequency of "hate at first sight" among military service members who later trust each other with their lives.

I got isolated reports of this phenomena in my clinical chair, so I decided to confirm the existence of hate at first sight as soon as I got the chance. I did get that chance eventually. When I was speaking to a group of more than two hundred active duty Marines, I asked them, "How many of you hated on sight another Marine that you now love like a brother and would trust with your life?" Hands shot up all over the room, confirmation that it is not uncommon for service members who love each other like family to have hated each other at first sight.

Based on the reports I heard from my patients, more often than you might think, a no-holds-barred fist fight was the first encounter of two veterans who now love each other like brothers. The logical conclusion to draw from this observation is that the trust formed between service members is not necessarily a result of compatible or similar personalities.

If baseline personality factors do not account for the love and trust that develops, then it follows that trust must be relatively more tied to the experiences that shape relationships among fellow members of the tribe. In other words, the experience of military service forges an indescribably deep bond of trust, creating a sense of tribe, even between people who have vastly different personalities and personal values.

What develops this kind of trust? Like many things, it's multicausal, but some of the major factors include the resocialization of service members, a common language, a unique set of group experiences, an orientation to a shared mission, and a shift away from an individual identity to collective identity. The elements of bonding have been the subject of social psychology research. One of the classic social psychology projects, the "Robber's Cave Study"[65] took a group of twelve-year old boys and separated them into two camps. Experimenters encouraged them to bond by having them engage in collective tasks. Each group gave itself a name and quickly established its own subculture and social norms.

When the two groups were later pitted against each other in competitive ways, they became so hostile to each other that the researchers had to separate them (hate at first sight on a massive scale). This led the researchers to consider not only how subcultures form but also what has the power to overcome intense levels of intergroup hostility. A follow-up experiment brought the two groups together and required them to complete what social psychology researchers call a "superordinate task."[66]

A superordinate task is a task that requires interdependence for task completion (for example, a ropes course that cannot be navigated without cooperative behavior). The researchers found that the superordinate task was able to overcome the intense hostility that had previously existed between the two groups; the task effectively converted the two groups into one tribe. Military service is like one extremely lengthy superordinate task.

But this is not the only factor that creates such deep bonds between service members. In my first book, *Marriage, for Equals,* I did an analysis on how the TV program *The Bachelor* uses powerful psychological principles to make people "fall in love" with total strangers. As a fun exercise, once when I was leading a group on the topic of trust for veterans and their partners, we analyzed the multiple factors that cause people to "fall into trust" with each other in the military.

As I said previously, military training removes people from the life they once knew and fundamentally reconstitutes their attachment system. This is not an exhaustive list, but here are ten factors that help create the bond between service members and their military family:

1. Separation from the rest of society — a world that is narrowed to the people and relationships at hand.
2. The stripping of individuality identity to build towards a new shared identity as service members earn their Eagle, Globe and Anchor, Parachute Wings, Trident, or Commission.
3. Wearing the same outfit and having the same efficient haircut.
4. A new language — including a multitude of new words, concepts, and acronyms that align with a new cultural understanding.[67]
5. Instillation of a common set of values and a guiding ethos. For example, soldiers are instilled with the values of loyalty, duty, respect,

selfless service, honor, integrity, and personal courage; and Marines are instilled with the values of honor, courage, and commitment.

6. Challenges that cannot be overcome on an individual basis, but must be done in an interdependent way.
7. A culture of being each other's keepers.
8. Introduction of life-and-death stakes (using live fire in firearms training exercises, which requires service members to begin to trust each other with their lives).
9. Identification of a common enemy for all involved (depending on the war of the time).
10. The requirement of sacrifice of time with one's family to be away on mission or tasks needed for military service.

Understanding these psychological factors helps us understand why the trust between service members doesn't automatically transfer to loved ones at home (and why a veteran might actually feel closer to someone he initially hated on sight than to the love of his life whom he chose because of personality compatibility). Helping warriors extend trust to their "home front tribe" (as I call it) has been an important part of my work with veterans and military family members. The ability to create these bonds with family members is not only possible, but it can be life saving for some service members.

A full description of the programs I have built to help service members and their loved ones is beyond the scope of this book. (If you want to learn more, I included more of this material in *BEYOND THE MILITARY: A Leader's Handbook for Warrior Reintegration*). However, in the present context, I will share some parts of this work that help us understand trust development. Specifically, let's trace the line of trust in romantic relationship development as a contrast to the way that trust develops in the military context.

As I explained in my first book, *Marriage, for Equals*, successful long-term romantic partnerships go through three phases: the cocaine rush phase, the testing phase, and the tested romanticism phase. The cocaine rush phase is the initial period of intense, highly pleasurable bonding based on the mutual fantasy that you and the other person are each other's soulmates. A hallmark of the cocaine rush phase is that blind trust is extended between the two people in the relationship. The cocaine rush is a period of delightful mutual delusion based on very limited information about the potential for a relationship to go the distance. Lovers in the first stage of a relationship often highlight similarities, minimize differences, and selectively filter for evidence that they are each other's perfect match.

If differences do not come to light before a couple marries, the risk for postmarital disillusionment (and dissolution) is higher.[68] In an interesting way, conflict becomes critical to trust formation. In warfare, and in close relationships, trust forms "in the trenches" of conflict: it is *conflict* that allows us to evaluate whether another person is fundamentally trustworthy. For example, in therapy, a slight rupture, followed by a repair of the treatment alliance often leads to a much stronger relationship. I think this is because ruptures and repairs give us critical sources of information about how much we can trust each other to stay connected, show respect, and stick it out when the going is rough — things we would not know otherwise.

If sources of incompatibility and disagreement can come up before marriage, then each partner will have an opportunity to decide whether incompatible values and behaviors are ones they can live with or not. Essentially, conflict tests character. Depending on how it is handled, conflict can support our growth; it tells us about who we are as individuals and who we are in partnership with others.

In addition to assessing individual trustworthiness, there is the bigger question of whether we can trust ourselves as a couple to weather the storms that will come. Theorists and researchers refer to this as "relationship self-efficacy." In other words, do we feel confident that we can work through stress and conflict productively? This may seem obvious, but it's a very important point: We can't know the answer to this question without having some conflict. *How* we work through problems is often more important than the actual issue(s) we resolve.

Partners in successful marriages show core respect, recognize the validity of each other's thoughts and feelings, and make generous attributions for each other's behavior.[69] Conflict allows us to ask ourselves if we feel heard and respected despite a squall of negative emotions. Putting this together with my model of successful relationships, then, a major reason to wait out the cocaine rush phase of the relationship is to date for long enough to see if we can weather a few storms before we take the plunge together.

In fact, I strongly recommend that couples in the premarital phase of their relationship proactively ask each other lots of hard questions to set off some hidden land mines before they consider marriage.[70] Couples that set off some land mines up front benefit from some of the protection that comes from the way we idealize each other in the cocaine rush phase. That is, motivation to overcome barriers and find common ground is typically at peak levels before two people are legally bound to each other. Probable areas of future conflict can be identified, and respectful rules of engagement can be developed. Two people who go into their marriage knowing that they can stay connected despite conflict have a much better chance of staying married. So, fighting before marriage can be a very good thing.

The transition between the cocaine rush phase and the testing phase is marked by a mutual fall from grace. Common markers of the testing phase are differences of opinion, and observation of each other's flaws and personal struggles. During the testing phase, incompatibilities and differences in values surface. The fox in our gut, the private pain and shame we work to conceal during the cocaine rush phase, begins to reveal itself. Violations of trust (sometimes major, sometimes minor) and attachment wounds are also common during the testing phase. Couples need to work through the suffering they bring on each other without losing the underlying trust that is the lifeblood of long-term relationships. Couples need to approach, rather than avoid, these challenges and areas of struggle while staying intact as a functional team.

Can a marriage actually become stronger when couples are faced with the stressors of military life — things like frequent moves, separating and coming back together during cycles of deployment, or adjustment after military discharge? Absolutely. This can happen for several reasons. First, when we face challenges, "autopilot" settings are traded for manual control of the marriage. Stressors of the military life often force dramatic changes in roles. If expectations are not openly discussed on an ongoing basis, though, relationships will suffer.

In the best of circumstances, couples develop a much deeper level of communication than they had previously. Second, successfully navigating stressors can help couples build trust. As mentioned previously, we don't know who we can trust until we go to battle as a team. The process of working through challenges together can make two people a much stronger team than ever before. They can learn to support each other in more meaningful ways. They can develop a new level of intimacy. The testing phase can become the crucible that shapes battle-tested partnerships.

Finally, working through challenges allows us to see that our partner really has our back. Many of us vow to commit to our partners no matter what may come. Those who stick it out through challenging times show their partners every single day that this was not an empty vow. Over time, this kind of process can propel couples into becoming each other's soulmate. That is, while the idea of finding one's soulmate is just a fantasy of the cocaine rush phase, it is possible for two people to *become* soulmates. This is effectively what happens during the third stage of successful relationships, the tested romanticism phase.

Partnerships in the tested romanticism phase are grounded in security and a rare and special form of earned intimacy. Effective, respectful negotiation of challenges has become habitual. Thoughts of separation or divorce are completely alien. The partnership has become so multifaceted and the compatibilities so intricately dovetailed that one's spouse could never be replaced by anyone else.

Two individuals who have become perfect for and irreplaceable to each other have become soulmates. In other words, soulmates are two people who have become each other's one-in-a-billion, perfect match over time. In the final stages of marriage, the bond that can be created is a deeper, more satisfying level of love than anything that anyone encounters in the initial cocaine rush phase of a relationship.

In one sense, to make a comparison between the experiences of love at these two relationship stages is like comparing apples and oranges. I would argue that love of a deep and meaningful kind is only possible when based on real knowledge and the test of time. If being loved is based on being known for who you are and cherished despite your flaws, then the feelings people have during the initial cocaine rush phase of a relationship can't be love. These feelings would be some combination of other pleasurable things, like hope and attraction, or delusions of the soulmate variety. What feels a lot like love in the cocaine rush phase does not compare to the love that couples may enjoy in the final phase of an exceptional marriage.

If you doubt this is true, consider the difference between the giddy feelings of being in love with someone you've known for a short time and the feelings of love you would have for someone who has been your most trusted battle buddy for the past sixty years of your life — the person who has been by your side through thick and thin, who has believed in you and invested in you. The following image traces the development of trust through the three phases of successful relationships.

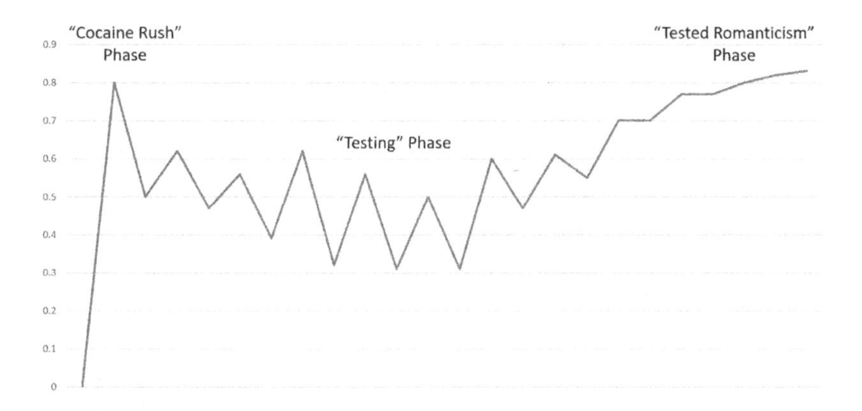

The Evolution of Battle-Tested Partnerships

As I said earlier, it is common for veterans to feel that no one will ever be closer than their military brothers and sisters. This mindset often leaves wives and other loved ones feeling like outsiders. Failure to develop the kind of deep trust we're talking about in marriage — to learn how to really have each other's back — undermines relationships. Of course, none of us marry someone expecting to get divorced someday. We generally marry each other in good faith with the intention of being each other's battle buddy in a metaphorical sense.

However, building trust and deepening intimacy is not a passive process; marriages don't get better as a function of time alone. They get better as a function of two people being able to stand without armor in each other's presence, especially during times of high stress. However, in my observation, warriors (and perhaps people in general?) keep their armor on with their partners for three main reasons, all of which can be traced to a kind of protective instinct.

The most common reason can be summed up in a statement like, "I am just trying to protect my loved one from worrying about me." That is, warriors may restrict what they share with their loved ones because they are afraid that it will cause their loved ones to feel more anxious about military or first-responder experiences. So, the intention here is a good one, but this doesn't achieve the intended effect. To put this in military speak, it's an example of good initiative, bad judgment.

As a rule, the anxiety we feel is often directly related to what we don't know. When we have a vague sense that something is wrong, but we lack any details to help us understand what the problem is, our anxiety goes way up. In military marriages, it is often the case that a spouse pushes for more disclosure in order to better understand the hidden pain of their military partner. If they cannot gain a good understanding of the problem, they are left with a chronically high level of anxiety. So, rather than protecting them, their partner is in fact unintentionally exposing them to a lot of anxiety.

Sometimes I get pushback on this point in the following way: "I don't want my partner to live with the images I have in my head." But there are ways to talk about problems without revealing specific details. For instance, rather than saying something like, "I was put in a situation where I had to shoot a little kid, and I can't forget the way he looked, lying on the ground with his insides spilling out," one could say, "I had to make some terrible choices that no one should have to make. I made those choices to protect my fellow Marines, but I am haunted by the memories of what happened. I know I had to protect my brothers, but the guilt is eating me alive. It makes me feel like I have done things for which I can't be forgiven." *This is what it sounds like to stand without armor with a partner.* Details aren't necessary for a loved one to understand the emotional pain of traumatic experiences. And without understanding the emotional impact of our experiences, a supportive spouse is powerless to help remove the fox in our gut.

A second reason why warriors (and people in general?) keep their armor on is to protect themselves. This motivation can be summed up in a statement like, "If my spouse really knew who I am, she would think I'm a monster." People who keep their armor on for this reason pay two very high costs: They lose out on the chance to build deep trust, and they lose the chance to feel unconditionally loved by their spouse. Their choice to conceal the fox in their gut introduces a split into the relationship and denies their spouse the opportunity to support them in their suffering. Again, a statement like the one above that shares the impact of past experiences without any details can help bring hidden pain out into the open.

This can be tricky, though. Disclosure can transform pain into healing very quickly, but only in cases where the partner is an emotionally safe and supportive person. I had the advantage of being able to assess the partners of the veterans I saw in my couples clinic. This helped me determine whether this intervention would be helpful or harmful.

I only did this intervention when my patient had a partner that I knew would be able and willing to listen without any judgment. These spouses were mature and emotionally safe. They were able to connect with their partner in a critically vulnerable time of need. They would be their partner's rock. I definitely wouldn't recommend this as a general strategy without some thoughtful assessment of how this interaction would play out in a given relationship. One of the tools in the handbook — the assessment of emotional safety — can help with this assessment, and because the stakes are so high, I would also recommend that this kind of conversation be facilitated by a skilled therapist.

The third reason that people keep their armor on is that they want to protect their loved ones from their own rage. Supporting couples around this issue warrants a much deeper exploration, and this will be the focus of the next chapter. To sum up this chapter, then, like functional military units, happy couples have a common language, and a shared identity and goals. Trust is formed in the trenches, and this requires that we approach conflict and go through battles together. When we do this, we form the tribe of those we love and trust.

In the book, *Tribe: On Homecoming and Belonging,* Sebastian Junger defines "tribe" as "the people you feel compelled to share the last of your food with."[71] I like this definition a lot, and I would add this element to the concept of tribe: Tribe is the people that you can stand before without armor. For many people, this might actually be more difficult than sharing their last piece of bread.

UNIVERSAL PRINCIPLES I LEARNED FROM WORKING WITH WARRIORS

1. ***The courage to stand without armor requires a different kind of courage than that required to operate in combat.***

   Courage in one domain does not always translate to courage in another. The courage required to engage in aggressive action may be fundamentally different from the courage it takes to inhibit aggressive or self-protective instincts and to stand before others in vulnerable ways, without any emotional armor.

2. ***There is often a strong connection between anger and attachment injuries.***

   When I see a high level of spillover anger in people, I know now that it's often helpful to ask about the status of important relationships. I knew about Sue Johnson's seminal work on developing secure attachments with approaches used in emotionally focused therapy. However, the concept of primal panic really came alive in case examples that looked more like anger management problems than panic/anxiety.

3. ***Trust formation is probably more a function of experiences than compatibility of personality and values.***

   People with vastly different and totally incompatible personalities can grow to deeply trust each other based on shared experiences. Trust forms in the trenches, and going through conflict actually helps us build trust. We learn things about ourselves and others that we would not know if we were to avoid conflict.

4. ***Stressors and challenges can break us down, but when we break down, there is the potential to build ourselves back up as a stronger couple than we were before.***

   Depending on how they are handled, breakdowns in relationships can result in battle-tested partnerships. Successfully facing challenges may accelerate the transition for some of us into the most satisfying phase of long-term romantic partnerships, the tested romanticism phase. During the cocaine rush phase, we do not arrive as soulmates, but we can become soulmates over time if we take off our armor and express our attachment needs directly.

QUESTIONS FOR REFLECTION AND APPLICATION

1. How does the concept of attachment wounds help explain some of the hidden pain of those who serve in our military and first responder populations? Thinking back to your own past relationships, how does the idea of attachment wounds help you understand the course of relationships that have not worked out?

2. As you reflect on the story of Joe and his wife, are there any unspoken attachment wounds in your current relationship(s)? How are these impacting trust and intimacy? What will it take to bring these issues out into the open, in a safe and productive way?

3. If we consider the factors that build trust between service members in the military, are there ways potentially that some of these factors can be migrated over to strong relationships with our home front tribe? For example, are there ways that couples can develop a common language, orient themselves to a set of shared life goals, and proactively work on superordinate tasks to develop themselves as an effective team?

4. Keeping our armor on is not a behavior that is unique to warriors; many of us choose this path over the path of vulnerability. Can you personally identify with any of the reasons why people may keep their armor on? For what reasons have you kept your own armor on in your close relationships?

5. The three-phase model of relationships was developed to apply to all relationships, not just those between warriors and their partners. In thinking about the descriptions of the three phases of relationships, can you mentally trace the transition between phases in your current relationship or your most recent past relationship? What kinds of

experiences have built trust and intimacy and moved you forward towards the tested romanticism phase of a relationship?

Don't forget to check out the handbook at the end of the book for further applications.

8

FRIENDLY FIRE

Early treatment approaches to addressing anger in coupled relationships have been strikingly off-base (pun intended). Before cognitive behavioral therapy came into wide favor as the go-to treatment for managing anger, clinical approaches were influenced by "catharsis theory." Catharsis theory suggested that physically venting anger (on a pillow, and so on) was the best way to manage it.

Some emotions do need to be expressed; for example, those who are grieving a loss can find relief and healing by expressing their grief. But anger doesn't work this way. Pairing anger with aggressive action makes an angry person progressively less inhibited and more aggressive over time; in fact, military training capitalizes on this. Anger and aggression are not the same thing.

While anger is a natural, common human emotion, aggression is action taken with a hostile intent. Based on catharsis theory, however, some couple's therapists used to give each partner a soft foam bat and instruct the couple to whack at each other until relief (or exhaustion!) sets in. What is comical about this intervention is that the same strategy has long been used to develop aggressive instincts among United States Marines. In training, Marines engage in combative drills using large sticks with padding on them called pugil sticks. Even the name "pugil stick" derives from combative terms: A "pugilist" is a boxer, and the associated word "pugnacious" means aggressive, combative, or hostile.

As our technology has advanced, we've gained a better understanding for how the brain works. An aerial view of the Grand Canyon provides a good analogy for how neural pathways develop in our brains. What is now a gaping chasm was carved out by water — the Colorado River, to be exact. The deepest canyons in the Grand Canyon system are those that have had the highest and strongest flow of water over time. In addition to the widest parts of the river, there are smaller offshoots where the land has been carved out by less powerful water flow.

These concepts can be translated onto the map of nerve pathways in our brain. Some pathways are habitually used, while others are like offshoots from the main pattern of behavior. When anger has become a habit and we encourage venting to "release" anger, we merely strengthen the force of the strongest pathways. Learning anger management skills is therefore about enhancing alternative ways of responding — recognizing the feeling of anger and disconnecting it from an impulsively aggressive response.

Military training is interesting to consider in light of this analogy. In one sense, military training develops aggressive impulses. A driving goal of recruit training is to decrease factors that inhibit aggressive responding, and some recruits have more preexisting barriers than others, who may already have a habit of aggressive responding. On the battlefield, other emotions, such as fear or grief, are channeled into aggressive action. Reducing the range of emotions in this way is not bad or good; effective combat action requires intense, directed focus.

However, repeatedly converting other emotions into aggressive responding helps explain why some veterans have a limited range of emotions after discharge. While in therapy, they might say things like, "I have two main emotions with nothing in between — happiness or anger" or "I either feel numb or angry." Part of the work in some cases may be helping patients reconnect with an expanded range of normal emotions.

At the same time, during military training, aggression is not developed in a way that removes all restraint; the goal of training is to help warriors achieve focused, strategic, disciplined aggressive responding. Military training develops the will and ability to dominate the enemy, but warriors are also taught rules of engagement and methods to systematically escalate the use of lethal force. It is not desirable for warriors to engage in frenzied, uncontrolled violence, as this puts everyone in greater danger.

The "berserk" state referenced in the work of Jonathan Shay as a "reckless frenzy … a beastlike fury" is an example of what is *not* desirable in combat operations.[72] As Shay describes, some warriors may enter a state of consciousness where they feel so invulnerable to harm that they take foolish risks that put themselves and others in mortal (and perhaps moral?) danger.

In contrast with this undesirable state, others get in the zone and feel a sense of steady, calm purpose as they draw from habitual skills learned during training. In the book *What It Is Like to Go to War*, author and combat Marine Karl Marlantes describes this state: "When I was fighting, I was usually in a white heat of total rationality, completely devoid of passion. I had a single overwhelming concern, to get the job done with minimal casualties to my side and stay alive doing it."[73]

Warriors who are most effective in battle keep their heads and can learn to see the battleground almost like a chess board. They stay in control of themselves and develop instincts about how the unit needs to be positioned to get the upper hand. Sometimes, I think that civilians may not fully understand that military training so strongly emphasizes and develops restraint, which can be a tremendous asset in therapy.

In other words, many times, as I have mentioned in previous chapters, warriors have already learned powerful ways to regulate their bodies that we may fail to appreciate. Many have learned to stay focused in chaotic, violent environments. They receive training to direct their attention in strategic ways. They are trained to solve problems in very stressful, high-stakes situations. Those who are skilled with firearms have learned to regulate their breathing and gently squeeze the trigger of their weapon to maximize accuracy. So, in my experience, many warriors already have many of the coping skills we may think we are introducing to them for the first time. Sometimes, it is better to remind them that they already have these skills.

A critical part of making a successful transition out of the military involves warriors extending a similar level of trust and love to their home front tribe. And as I have said before, developing this deep trust is a function of learning how to come together, and stay together, as one team in the heat of conflict.

Developing deep trust requires us to stand without armor — and *without weapons* — with our partners. In other words, protecting those we love from our own rage is critical. Unless we are taught otherwise, our natural response is to be overrun by strong emotions when we feel threatened, defect from being part of a team, ("Every man or woman for them-selves!") and vent our rage on our partners.

A relatively small number of us were raised by people who demonstrated how to navigate conflict without turning on each other. But many of us have not had a good model. I never had that model myself. It's not that my parents fought in openly hostile ways; their conflicts occurred behind the closed doors of my father's home office. I learned what I know about conflict first from observing many of the two hundred newlywed couples that were followed over four years of marriage in the Florida Project on Newlywed Marriage and Adult Development (FPNMAD).

Within the FPNMAD study, we asked couples to discuss topics that were a source of conflict in their relationship. After the first ten seconds, they forgot about the cameras. Something primal was at work. We coded their interactions and witnessed, at a granular level, the differences between couples who successfully break through conflict, and those who break down in conflict.

I continued to learn about stress and conflict in other ways. For my dissertation, I studied the effects of stress on marriages in an aggregated sample of more than 145,000 partnered individuals. After completing my doctoral degree, I reached out to my networks (mostly Harvard graduates) and collected additional data with the Lifestyle Poll, a survey with more than two hundred questions. A sample of more than 1,200 women, spanning eight graduating classes at Harvard, completed the Lifestyle Poll. I couldn't pay them for their time — the whole survey was run on a budget of $500. Since they didn't do it for money, I think they did it because there was a shared desire among us to better understand these things — to reflect on how we were forming our closest relationships and navigating stress and conflict.

When I worked at the VA, I took what I had learned from a decade of focusing on close relationships and adapted it for military couples. What follows is an overview of some of the most important principles to help military (and civilian) couples to successfully navigate conflict.

Avoiding Conflict Has Hidden Costs

First, we often need to expand our understanding of the role and value of conflict. Conflict is the most natural, inevitable thing in the world. Navigating conflict well deepens intimacy and builds strong relationships. As I mentioned earlier, trust is theoretical until the first firefight.

It is during conflict that we learn new things about ourselves, our partners, and our relationship. Through conflict, there is the potential to become a more effective team than we were before. But many of us are terrified to engage in conflict. This is no less true for combat veterans than for civilians. In fact, in my experience, combat veterans are often *much more afraid* to engage in conflict with their partners for fear of their own anger.

However, avoiding conflict — whatever the reason — has hidden costs. These hidden costs do not often register for many years (like other lifestyle decisions that build to a head over many years). When a couple habitually avoids conflict, they create a potential "sinkhole" issue in the relationship. Sinkholes are common in states like Florida where the topsoil sits over layers of fine sand. Over time, hidden streams of water — sometimes just trickles — erode the sand layers under the surface. What looks solid on top looks like Uncle Milton's ant farm underneath, until one day, the bottom drops out. In Florida, sinkholes were known to drop below houses, semitrucks, sometimes even a solitary jogger. Avoiding conflict erodes intimacy and trust, and places a relationship on unstable ground. In conflict-avoidant relationships, it is often just a matter of time before the bottom drops out.

Aggressive Behavior Comes from Different Sources

A helpful distinction to draw is whether anger is more impulsive/reactive or intentional/premeditated. People whose anger is intentional and premeditated don't necessarily even have anger control issues; they may take aggressive action while in a totally calm and focused state. They like dominating others and feel the right to be aggressive. They may have enlisted in the military because they always enjoyed violence, and military training only further honed their capabilities for aggressive responding.

In domestic violence scenarios, such individuals treat their partners like property. They show little genuine remorse. The vast majority of veterans I treated were not this way, but they had impulsive/reactive anger. They felt helpless and ashamed when they lost control of themselves. Some isolated themselves out of a fear of being triggered and suffering negative consequences as a result of losing control ("I don't want to end up in jail because some jerk triggers me"). They were protective by nature and wanted to protect their loved ones from their own rage.

In the marital literature, a clear distinction is made between chronic, predatory violent behavior and common couples violence. "Common couples violence" is incredibly common as the name would suggest. In some cases, both partners may be involved,[74] and it may include pushing, shoving, restraining, or sometimes even hitting.

Let's consider the case of Rick (not his real name) and his wife, Lara (also not her real name). Rick had returned from a combat deployment eight months prior. Both partners agreed that before his most recent deployment, he had had no particular challenges with anger management. But now his self-control seemed to be slipping. Initially, he would yell at Lara in an intimidating way. This had turned into verbal abuse. Recently, he had pushed Lara against a wall, and then had quickly withdrawn, disappearing for several hours, horrified by his own behavior.

This is not to say that someone who is violent is in fact the victim of the situation. However, what I did observe is that individuals may become flooded with strong emotions and act in impulsive ways that are not in line with their general character. When this happens in the case of veterans like Rick, they express an overwhelming feeling of horror ("This rage comes over me, and it's like I turn into a monster. I see her face and she is so scared. I hate it."). After their anger subsides, people like Rick feel deep shame. When thinking about the possibility of future anger episodes, they feel dread. Moreover, instead of reacting with fear, their partner typically reacts with confusion.

Sometimes, in couples therapy sessions, their partner often withholds disclosing what happened because they do not want the veteran (who is generally loving) to be perceived as a "monster." In these cases, the warrior's basic personality is not characterized by strong narcissistic or antisocial elements. Instead, such behavior represents the temporary hijacking of higher values when a primitive drive arises. Like Rick, they may feel psychologically flooded or cornered in some way. In this state of mind, they may suddenly shove or slap their partner and then express genuine horror for having done so.

In cases like this, it is very important to avoid inducing further shame because shame can be related to the emergence of suicidal ideation for some veterans ("It's like I turn into a monster" can quickly become the thought, "I am the problem that needs to be taken out"). So, exploring the impact of his anger on his wife in a way that creates more shame is a really bad idea; he already feels a level of toxic shame that could be dangerous if it is not addressed. Is it possible to deepen Rick's understanding of the impact of violence on safety and trust in the marriage without inducing shame? Yes. Here is how I did it with my patients:

> I want you to imagine that we've been meeting for nearly a year. We've had really good sessions every time we've met. You have always felt safe here. But then one day, without any warning, you come into my office, and I suddenly throat punch you. So you tell my boss that you want to be reassigned to a new therapist, and I react with shock. Why would you feel unsafe with me now? We have been meeting for well over a year. The past thirty sessions were all completely safe. I only throat punched you once, so you really ought to get over it.

This effectively demonstrates the impact of violent behavior in a respectful, nonshaming way that lands with veterans. Through this analogy, they are able to see that any violent behavior — even impulsive, unplanned acts — has a long-term negative impact on their partner's sense of safety and security.

Moving Towards Emotional Self-Mastery

What Rick needs is to develop a sense of control and power. He needs to feel that he has the skills to protect his wife from his own rage. He needs to feel that he can regulate his own system. This is true not only for Rick but also for Lara. The end state for both partners is to develop emotional self-mastery and meta-awareness of their habitual patterns. Emotional self-mastery is a skill, and it can be developed — just as service members are trained to balance aggressive responding with self-control.

Awareness is always the first component of skill building. Well over a decade ago, when primitive watches with heart-rate monitors were just coming onto the market, I used this tool to help patients develop emotional self-mastery. The intervention was quite simple: Take two weeks to get a spectrum of baseline data, for example, heart rate upon waking from a peaceful sleep, heart rate when awakening after a nightmare, heart rate when relaxed, and heart rate when angered. Interestingly, for some warriors, a lower heart rate, not a higher one, was most associated with destructive rage.

So, the key was to measure the heart-rate values that were reliably associated with various mind states. This allowed my patients to immediately feel a sense of control and predictability as they worked on guessing their heart rate in light of their level of irritability/anger. They then folded in experiments to help themselves downregulate.

The ways and means of down-regulation are as varied as people themselves, so the intervention was built to allow them to lead themselves in discovering what worked for them. For some, it was vigorous physical exertion but not while thinking of the violent ways they would like to engage their partners. For others, it was deep breathing, listening to music with strong positive emotional associations, going surfing and allowing the swelling waves to bring them to a meditative state, calling a friend to get an outside perspective, and so on.

Once these elements were well developed, they had a toehold into the kind of meta mental state that is required for emotional self-mastery. Specifically, it became possible to use this crude biofeedback tool — a primitive heart-rate monitor — to give them biologically based data on when they can productively engage in conflict with their partners. If their heart rate were too high or too low, then they knew that protecting their partner from their rage meant making a tactical withdrawal (which I'll explain in more detail shortly) for a space of time.

Understanding the Alligator Brain Mode

Another helpful frame is the story and example of an alligator I once met who was named Mojo. Mojo was a bull gator — the barrel-chested alpha (i.e., dominant) alligator within a famous family of alligators that lived two miles from my home in Florida. Visitors came in throngs to the Kanapaha Botanical Gardens to see Mojo and his growing family. Like other bull gators, Mojo grew about a foot a year and spent his days lazily sunning himself on the banks of the lily pad pond. I happened to visit him two weeks before he made the local news.

With no barrier between us, I walked on the path five feet away from where he had settled down for a midday siesta. We were so close that I smelled him — a bit dank, musty in an organic way, with a slight odor of baked ceramic tiles. Two weeks later, he was dragged up from the bottom of the pond and killed. His stomach was cut open to retrieve the arm of the park's lead custodian. The arm was so mangled that it could not be reattached. To his credit, the custodian was philosophical about losing his arm. He reflected on how Mojo's act of aggression was not premeditated; it was based on the animal instinct to react defensively to a perceived threat. So it is with so many couples.

At the time, I was studying human emotion, and the Mojo attack fully cemented this idea: We all have an alligator brain in our skulls. Stacked on top of our alligator brain — what biologists sometimes call the "reptilian brain stem" — is the part of our brain that makes us fully human. The upper part of our brain, the executive functioning center, is meant to control our behavior in most circumstances. This part of our brain allows us to plan, strategize, and critically evaluate how to go after what we want without damaging those we love.

What follows is not a scientifically accurate description, but rather a narrative that illuminates how rage works. It is an explanation that has helped many of my patients. First, divide the brain into just two parts for a moment — the alligator brain and the executive functioning center.

Now imagine that there is a very thick, solid iron gate on thick hinges between the two parts of the brain. When we are consumed by rage, a wave of chemicals pushes the gate between the two parts closed. We are hijacked by our alligator brain — the same one that controlled Mojo when he literally bit off the hand that fed him. In "Mojo mode," we see red.

Our vision tunnels, and the feeling of threat compels us to see our partner as a hostile combatant rather than the person who we committed to honor and love for the rest of our lives. We say things that later burn us with shame, cruel things that our partners often remember for many years. We inflict attachment wounds and hack away at the roots of security in our relationship. We tell our partner that we are not on their team, and our behavior shows them that we are only for ourselves. We cannot access our executive functioning center, the part that allows us to consider options for responding. We are overrun by rage and feel compelled to annihilate the perceived threat.

If we can build awareness that we are in "Mojo mode," however, we can make a tactical withdrawal to regain our emotional self-mastery. Even if we did nothing fancy — no soothing relaxation exercises, no guided meditation, no downward dog yoga poses, no cognitive behavioral therapy thought-stopping sheets — and we simply just waited with the goal of regulating our emotional state, we would see the iron gate swing back open again.

We would know that our gate was opening up again when our vision widens, when we see clearly with a range of colors (not just red or grey fuzz), and we begin to think of options for creative responses to the situation at hand. When we are no longer in "Mojo mode," we can reengage without destroying the feelings of love and security in our relationship.

In fact, in my experience, couples don't often need therapists to suggest specific solutions for their conflicts; they quite easily generate a number of creative ways to resolve conflicts once they are both in the right mind state. In most cases, what couples therapists do is create a radically safe space that protects the couple from "friendly fire" casualties so that they can progress through conflicts.

The Art of Making a Tactical Withdrawal

When we are in "Mojo mode," the wise course of action is to detach from conflict for a space of time. To emphasize the difference between passive submission (undesirable), conflict avoidance (undesirable), and protecting loved ones from our own rage (desirable), I developed the concept of "tactical withdrawal." Tactical withdrawal is fundamentally honorable. It is what we do when we want to develop emotional self-mastery. In order to be effective, however, detachment must be done in a way that creates a stronger attachment.

As I have mentioned in an earlier chapter, the withdrawal of a primary attachment figure can create what Dr. Sue Johnson has called "primal panic." This is what happens by default, unless care is taken to explain the detachment in a way that deepens trust. An example may help. Imagine you are in the middle of a heated conflict, and your partner says, "I am getting too angry, and I need to go calm myself down before I say or do something that I don't intend. I need this time to calm down because I love you and I don't want to hurt you, or us. I will come back when I am calm, and we can continue this then."

Or here is another way to get to the same end: "We are doing this again. I don't want us to hurt each other in this way. I'm going to go calm down. Let's try again when we're both calmer."

It can be hard to touch our partners when we are angry, but it can be the most powerful thing we can do during conflict. Gentle, loving physical touch — even a hand placed on an arm, can help us reregulate and may communicate love and trust more deeply than words can. It bears repeating that tactical withdrawal must never, ever be used to avoid conflict. The partner who initiates a tactical withdrawal must reengage when they are in a more productive mind state. Otherwise, trust is broken.

A tactical withdrawal is, by definition, one that is temporary. The time apart allows for a shift to a more productive state of mind, followed by a strategic reengagement. Some of my patients have found it helpful to lead themselves through a simple thought exercise, asking themselves questions like:

- What made that feel so hurtful to me?
- Is this about the thing we're fighting about now, or older stuff that is still impacting me? If so, what?
- What do I want? What is my end state?
- How can I explain what I want to my partner in a way that is respectful — that treats them like my team member or battle buddy?

Using Existing Assets

For military couples, I have also used assets they already have developed, like five-paragraph orders and SMEAC.[75] SMEAC stands for situation, mission, execution, administration/logistics, and command/signal. SMEAC is a tool used in the military to organize a mission-related response or overcome a mission-related challenge.

During the session where this first emerged as a tool, I was with a Marine Corps veteran with approximately ten combat deployments. The strain in his relationship was overwhelming, and he was becoming emotionally dysregulated during one very difficult session. I asked him, "Is there any tool you learned during the military that can help you organize the current chaos in your mind? What did you use to organize the chaotic variables of fluid situations during combat operations?"

His eyes focused and his head cleared. His face changed. He said, "Yes, of course! SMEAC." He taught me the concept of SMEAC — situation, mission, execution, administration/logistics, command/signal — and we modified it for use in his close relationship. Here is an explanation of how we applied this:

Situation (S) translated to the situation of both partners in the relationship as members of the same team.

The Mission (M) translated to the general goal for this Marine and his partner to regain a solid footing for their relationship. This involved detailed discussion of the desired end state and the vision for how he would like to interact with his partner.

Execution (E) stood for what he needed to do to move his relationship in the right direction. Some actions required input from his partner, while others required him to focus on himself. For example, he could request that his partner give him twenty minutes of wind-down time at the end of each day after coming home from his very stressful job. A self-focused goal might be developing greater emotional control during conflicts.

Administration (A) is the people and materials needed to accomplish his objective, related to developing his team of support. We called this his fireteam because in the Marine Corps, Marines train in coordinated groups of four warriors.

Finally, Command/Signal (C) helped us lay out a plan for communication and feedback to ensure that he was progressing towards his goals.

Using tools like this that may already be very familiar to warriors provides clarity and a way forward. It was yet another powerful illustration on my path to becoming "Doc Springer" — another reminder that we may not need to reinvent the wheel, but we may just need to ask the right questions to unlock the assets our patients already have.

The Way to Ask for Change

In addition to managing our own emotions, another critical skill is learning how to ask for change. A fellow graduate student in the Ben Karney lab brought clarity and wisdom to the ongoing debate: In our close relationships, do we want to be known for who we are, warts and all, and loved despite our flaws, or do we want to perceived by our partners in a slightly idealized way?[76]

For many years, this debate filled the pages of a slew of academic journals until my colleague came along and pointed out that people want *both.* In other words, we want to be seen and known for who we are, flaws included, *and* we want to be slightly idealized, seen through the tint of rose-colored glasses, by our partners.

In translating this research into practice, I have observed that relationships occur at two levels — the global and specific levels. The *G* (global) level refers to the overarching sense we have of our partners — things like whether they are a desirable partner or not, and things that capture their character as a whole. On the *S* (specific) level of relationships, are all the behaviors that happen in relationships — some good; some bad; some not bad or good, just incompatible between partners.

The essence then of being a "battle buddy" in one's closest relationship is to maintain a solid, positive *G*. When we first meet our partners, *G* is rock solid — in fact, it is "pathologically secure," as we idealize our partners in the first flush of love, overlooking all kinds of specific behaviors that are negative or incompatible.

As we transition from the cocaine rush to the testing phase of our relationship, we start to notice a whole range of negative and incompatible *S* behaviors, which can create a shaky *G*. In other words, we may start to wonder if our partner really is a desirable catch or not. During the testing phase, we start to engage in conflict, and if we can accelerate into conflict and navigate it skillfully, we will emerge with a positive *G* that is based on real data, rather than the idealization and wishful thinking of the cocaine rush phase.

Essential to navigating this skillfully is the ability to ask for changes in a way that protects our partner at the global level. If we can do this, we can transform all kinds of negative interactive behaviors at the specific level. Again, an example may help. Let's say that a chronic stressor in our relationship is excessive spending from a joint checking account without agreement by both parties. Asking for change while protecting our partner at the global level might look like this:

> I love you, and I'm proud of how we're handling [specific examples of challenges already overcome]. We are becoming a stronger team, and I know that you have my back. When you spend more than $50 from our joint account without checking with me first, I start to get ulcers when I look at our checking account balance. Can we please agree to check with each other before making any purchases over $50? Thank you for looking out for me in this way.

By doing this, one has effectively shored up one's partner at the global level while asking for changes at the specific level. This kind of approach is much less likely to generate unproductive, rage-state conflict.

Managers of successful companies use a variant of this technique when giving corrective feedback to their employees. They start with a positive statement, give the corrective feedback, and then end with a positive statement. It's the classic "turd sandwich." In any case, successful managers are skilled turd sandwich artists. They do it because it works, and it can help us ask for change in our close relationships as well.

One-Up, One-Down Relationships

Finally, to wrap up this chapter on building healthy patterns at home, it is important to touch on a subject that can be sensitive: All too often in military partnerships, I have observed a tendency for an imbalanced relationship, where one person is consistently the caregiver for the other. I am not referring to the noble calling of military spouses who step up to support their injured partners as needed, but a more nuanced pattern that some couples fall into, to their detriment.

Sometimes this pattern is an extension of the ethos shared by active duty warrior families, where the home front tribe often cultivates a life that is centered on being supportive of their deployed warrior. Military families may be told to handle all the stress at home so that their deployed loved one is not distracted by stressors at home. And this may indeed be necessary during seasons of deployment, as a distracted warrior can be an impaired warrior. However, if this pattern continues, it will create a parent-child relationship rather than a partnership of warrior husband and wife (or warrior partners, as the case may be).

In the long run, this pattern of emotional caregiving depletes the inner resources of the caregiver and atrophies the inner strength of the partner they are supporting, who would be better served to exercise the muscles of self-mastery and self-direction. It creates a "one-up, one-down" relationship that isn't satisfying to either partner. This also absolutely impacts the capacity to enjoy a healthy sex life. To break this pattern, partners must become battle buddies who support each other in reciprocal ways. To put it another way, there can be no "identified patient" in the relationship, but rather two individuals who have come together to have each other's back through the storms that life brings.

If this unhelpful one-up, one-down pattern is present, it often requires the non-caregiving partner in the relationship to change the pattern that has been at play. Change often happens when warriors take off their armor and follow this disclosure with an invitation to help shoulder the emotional burdens of their partner in return. When this happens, we may observe a funny irony about bearing each other's emotional burdens: Helping carry the emotional burdens of a partner often means doing absolutely nothing but listening with love and acceptance. This is often harder to do than it is to take action to try to solve a partner's stressors.

People of action — which is the case for many warriors — want to *do* something when someone they love is suffering. However, even the act of advising a course of action, let alone managing another person's challenges, disrupts the healthiest form of relationship between two battle buddies. Advising, counseling, and giving advice quickly shifts the relationship from one between two battle buddies to a one-up, one-down relationship.

The recipient of advice may feel disrespected because, while it may not be intentional, their partner has essentially communicated this sentiment: "You can't handle your own challenges. I can manage them better than you can. From my place of superior wisdom, here is what you ought to do." That is why scores of women for many centuries have repeatedly told their husbands, "Look, I don't need you to solve my problems. I just want you to listen to me."

Ultimately, being an effective battle buddy means trusting in the competence of your partner, or their ability to develop their competence, while letting them know that you have their back. This allows them to draw from your strength to discover their own strength from within. If you do this for your partner, over time, you will become their soul mate, the irreplaceable person that will become their one-in-a-billion perfect match.

UNIVERSAL PRINCIPLES I LEARNED FROM WORKING WITH WARRIORS

1. ***Some aggressive behavior is deeply unintentional.***

   It is critical to understand the difference between premeditated, intentional aggression and the type of aggression that comes from an individual who is flooded with strong emotions. The prognosis for people who are unintentionally aggressive is generally quite hopeful. Helping people not give themselves permission to vent their rage on their loved ones is important, but this must be done without shaming. Those who are unintentionally aggressive can work towards greater emotional self-mastery by applying some fairly basic principles, as described in this chapter.

2. ***All of us have an alligator brain, and therefore, we can all go into alligator mode given the right (wrong?) triggers.***

   Because we all have a reptilian brain stem below our higher-thinking brain, it is therefore possible for all of us to go into "alligator mode" when we are triggered. Understanding this and acknowledging our own capacity for unrestrained aggression may help others feel less shame in working to gain more emotional self-mastery.

3. ***"Turd sandwiches" can protect different kinds of relationships.***

   Every relationship happens on two levels — the global level (*G*) of how we perceive our partners' character and overall desirability as a partner, and the specific level (*S*). Understanding this allows us to be more intentional about protecting our partners at the global level. The technique of serving up a "turd sandwich" that has long been used by effective business leaders can be deployed to help us ask for change in our close relationships.

4. ***Helping to shoulder the emotional burdens of our partners often requires us to do nothing at all.***

   It is an odd thing to put into words, but true nonetheless, that helping to shoulder others' burdens often requires us to do nothing at all other than listen and walk with them. Others in our lives may feel disrespected in a way that can be hard to identify when we give them advice. However, our steady supportive presence allows them to draw from our strength to build their own inner strength to overcome their challenges.

QUESTIONS FOR REFLECTION AND APPLICATION

1. Many within the military and first responder communities learn how to channel aggressive impulses. How would you summarize your relationship with your own anger? Are you comfortable with it? Do you fear it? How has your anger been connected to your past aggressive behavior? How can making these connections help you support others who are working with their anger?

2. Given that Marine Corps training uses pugil sticks to heighten aggressive responding, this intervention is unlikely to help us manage anger well in our close relationships. If our goal is to gain emotional self-mastery, what is the difference between venting our anger on a person (verbally, with a foam bat, etc.) and expending energy (doing a physically exhausting workout) in order to self-regulate strong emotions?

3. Many of my patients felt deep shame after losing control of their anger. Have you ever lost control of your anger and then felt ashamed after the fact? If so, how did you address the feelings of shame (if you did)? What have past conflicts taught you about yourself and other people that you would not have known otherwise?

4. In most cases, the anger I have worked with in the veteran and first responder populations has been reactive, rather than premeditated. Can you think of examples from your own life of how aggressive behavior can come from different places — that some people are aggressive in a premeditated, intentionally predatory way, while others lash out when they feel threatened? What are the implications of understanding these very different sources of aggressive behavior?

5. Being known for who we are, and loved despite our flaws, is a human need for veterans and civilians alike. Do you agree with the idea that

in our closest relationships, we want to be both known for who we are, warts and all, and slightly idealized by our partners? If so, how does this insight help us navigate conflict while protecting our loved ones' sense of security and value in the relationship?

Check out the handbook at the end of the book for further ways to apply this content.

9

OUR GREATEST POWER

To launch this reflection on a power greater than despair, travel with me to the Valley of Death, in the Korengal region of Afghanistan. As shown in the documentary films of Sebastian Junger and Nick Quested, what you would see is an isolated group of soldiers defending a crudely outfitted, remote outpost in the midst of intensely hostile territory. The living quarters are little more than a hole dug out of the side of a mountain.

The Valley of Death was so named because so many soldiers have been either killed or maimed there. As Misha Pemble-Belkin, a soldier in the film *Korengal* put it, "Pretty much every day we got in a firefight. Every day someone was trying to kill us. Our friends were getting shot next to us. People lost their arms ... lost their legs. We had our friends get killed ... I never thought I was going to make it out of the valley alive." An environment like this exacts a massive psychological toll on service members.

Soldiers in the Korengal must weather physical and mental exhaustion, long periods of mind-numbing boredom, the constant threat of severe injuries or death, and the helplessness and gut-wrenching grief of seeing their brothers injured and killed. It seems only natural that such conditions could easily create a deep sense of despair and hopelessness.

Yet in this scenario, and others like it, suicide is quite rare. In fact, in a study exploring the impact of deployment on suicide rates in a sample of 3.9 million service members, no association was found between deployment and increased suicide risk.[77] How can we make any sense of these two seemingly contradictory notions? Let's take a closer look at the themes in Junger's interviews of soldiers deployed to the Korengal Valley.

Several soldiers reflect on their time together and the bonds they shared with a sense of deep yearning. For example, Misha Pemble-Belkin, who was quoted earlier, said "I will never be as close with anybody else in the world." Miguel Cortes says, "We're closer than a family would be ... I would throw myself on a grenade, and the guys know that I would, without hesitation." Kyle Steiner says, "I would do anything for them. I would walk across the country to help them change a tire in a heartbeat ... You might have your family's blood running through your veins, but you didn't shed it with them." Sterling Jones leaves us with this truth: "I'm not doing this for my country ... truthfully, I couldn't give a sh-t what anybody thinks, except for the guys to my right and left." These statements speak to the bonds of love and trust among those in the "tribe" of warriors (hereafter referred to as "the power of tribe"), a power that I have repeatedly witnessed to be greater than despair.

Specifically, as I have also observed during several years of frontline clinical work, what Junger captured in *Korengal* is a timeless truth for many combat warfighters. Stories and statements like these were frequently shared by my patients. I'll always remember the case of a Japanese American World War II patient who asked me to share his story before he passed away. It was a story I had never heard, full of ugly, hidden twists and turns, truly a fox in the gut of American ideals.

His story is this. After Pearl Harbor, he and his brothers were classified as enemy aliens within their own country. In effect, this means that they were designated as unfit to serve in the United States military. He and his family were routed from their home and packed off to a detention processing center in Turlock, California.

From there, they were moved to a permanent internment camp in the Arizona desert. He remembered the stench from the heat and proximity of so many families living in converted horse stalls, with only sheets to separate them for privacy. After months of enduring subhuman living conditions, he and his brother were told that they had to prove that they were not Japanese sympathizers. They were forced to fill out a loyalty questionnaire which was then used to draft them into an all Japanese American combat unit called the 442nd Infantry Regiment. Next, they were shipped off to a training camp with rusty tap water and leaking ceilings, where they were issued uniforms and gear that had been left over or cast off from other units.

After training, they sailed for war, leaving from the New York Harbor. As they passed Ellis Island, they were instructed by their command to get below decks because they had not earned the right to view the Statue of Liberty. The 442nd were treated as utterly expendable, sent on the deadliest missions to rescue or support other units that were hopelessly surrounded by enemy forces. They suffered so many losses that the entire regiment had to be replaced two times over. Within the ranks of the fourteen thousand to eighteen thousand who served in the 442nd, more than 9,400 purple hearts were awarded for injuries sustained in battle.

They fought a war on two fronts at the same time — the bloody war that claimed my patient's older brother along with legions of loyal Japanese American citizens, and a war on our racist, fear-based response to Pearl Harbor. Based on his story, you might think that my patient would look back on his military service with bitterness or anger. Yet, when I asked about his time in country, his face softened, and he said this: "When I went into combat, I think that was probably the best time of my life, even though I was afraid. I never felt so close to people before that time or ever again."

It is clear that these bonds between our warriors are sacred and very special. But do they have the power to protect us from despair that has already seeped deep into our hearts? Returning to the example of Junger's work in the film *Korengal,* there is an account of a soldier who finds himself deep in a tunnel of despair:

> The brothers we lost actually hit me pretty hard. I would think about the guys that would go down and there was a time when I didn't care about anything. I didn't care if I lived or died. I didn't care if I got shot … that's how bad it got … there was times when I would actually shoot back and not duck … I would run in the open just not caring.

First, let's notice here that it is not anxiety, but rather grief and loss, that precipitates this soldier's despair. The helpless, overwhelming grief of losing his brothers is the fox in his gut that leads him into a dangerously suicidal mode. The line between emotional apathy and intentional self-harm gets very fuzzy in a place like the Valley of Death. In the Korengal, the behaviors he describes are like engaging in repeated attempts to end the pain of his grief with a "death by cop" type of plan, substituting enemy insurgents for police officers.

Yet here again, if we listen closely, we see how the power of tribe saved him and helped pull him out of this tunnel of despair. Consider the rest of what he said, and take particular notice of the parts that have been highlighted:

> There was a time when I didn't care if I got shot … that's how bad it got. It *took quite a few people to actually pick me back up* … I started doing what I was supposed to be doing when someone told me, "If you go down … someone *else* could get shot."

Here is how I translate his statement: *I was in such a dark and hopeless place that I was not willing to live for myself, but when my tribe made it clear that my death would directly impact them, I regained the will to stay in the fight for those I vowed to protect.*

The power of tribe repeatedly surfaced in the stories of near-death experiences among my patients. I realized that I was hearing two categories of stories that were essentially brushes with death. On the one hand, several of my patients shared accounts of being hit by an IED or other potentially lethal projectile while in the combat zone. In these accounts, their fellow soldiers or Marines would run into danger to get them to safety. Their brothers- and sisters-in-arms would stay with them, calling in a medic while saying things like, "I'm right here. Look at me. Stay with me. You're going to be okay!"

Commonly, time would slow down, and the faces and voices of loved ones would mentally appear, urging them to stay in the fight — maybe the face of a child or a spouse imploring them to come home safely. Sometimes, a fellow warrior who had previously fallen in battle would mentally appear to infuse them with the will to fight, saying things like, "The guys need you!" or "You don't have permission to die!" Many expressed that these visitations gave them the will to fight for life, despite potentially lethal injuries.

The stories of my patients' past suicide attempts were different. In these types of near-death experiences, when individuals are in the grip of a suicidal crisis, on the ropes in the fight with their demons, there was commonly a profound detachment from loved ones. This helps us understand how a person can honestly, sincerely say, "I would never attempt suicide" one week (and mean it) and then get into a head space where self-destruction somehow seems like the right choice the following week.

Rather than hearing the voices and seeing the faces of loved ones, their thoughts obsessively looped on the theme of being a burden, a danger, or a liability to those they love. Their brains would actively make a case for how others will not really miss them or that in the long run, those they love would be better off without them somehow.

Of course, loved ones would often vehemently disagree with this if they had had the opportunity. But the perceptions of a person in a suicidal mode are extremely distorted. Towards the end of a tunnel of despair, people see suicide as the only "logical" choice, the same way that people who are struggling with advanced stage anorexia see themselves as fat.

Once I noticed these divergent themes in these two categories of near-death accounts, I saw that what I was hearing mapped onto what I was seeing as a timeless truth: *In battles with our demons, attachment to those we love and trust has a power that can help us survive the obliterating pain of despair. This is the power of tribe. This may be the most important takeaway in this whole book.*

If we want to get any real traction in the battle to keep more of our citizens in the fight, it is critical for us to grab this insight and apply it to the work of suicide prevention: *When we connect, we survive.* Warriors are not generally self-protective by nature, but they have a very strong protective instinct for other people. As a rule, many of our warfighters, like the soldiers in Junger's films, would walk into a kill zone to save a fallen comrade-in-arms. Many of our nation's service members enlisted in part because of an instinct to protect and defend those they love.

This principle applies to warriors in the conventional sense of the word, and also to a number of other people who are constructed in the same way. They are our first responders, our firefighters, our police officers. They are the mothers and fathers, aunts and uncles, and aging grandparents whose will to live comes from the fact that others need them to stay in the fight. They may not be willing to live for themselves at times, but reactivating their attachment to those who need them may pull them out of a tunnel of despair.

Recognizing the power of these attachments led to further insights that have shifted the way I see the work of suicide prevention: Instead of asking "How can we come up with a plan to help you pull yourself out of a crisis?" a better question might be, "How can we help you draw from the strength of your tribe to give you the will to stay in the fight?"

This line of thinking led me to wonder about several additional questions, such as: What if we've been coming at the tragedy of the suicide losses we are seeing in our society from the wrong angle? Maybe the model we've been using is so pervasive that we've forgotten to continually test the faults in its most basic assumptions? What if the model we've been using is nowhere near powerful enough to wage an effective war on despair?

Framed in this way, it becomes clear that as a society, for several decades now, we have been using a "professional defender" model of suicide prevention. The professional defender model says that suicidal thoughts and feelings are experts-only issues. By virtue of our training, licensed professional therapists are seen as having the required skills to help people effectively wage war against hopelessness.

We have invested millions of dollars in public campaigns to raise awareness of suicide. We have also seen the emergence of several training programs to help nonprofessionals ask questions when they see potential signs of suicide risk. But ultimately, the fundamental goal that unifies our current strategies is to assess risk and bridge to care with a professional. The therapy relationship and the clinical treatment plan is thought to be the active ingredient in saving a life. So, our current approach often boils down to a "get thee to a doctor" mentality.

To be fair, licensed professionals do have substantial assets to bring to this fight. Seasoned professionals often have a good level of comfort with asking questions about suicide risk. Asking questions about risk is part of our job description. We are familiar with a number of assessment tools designed to identify suicide risk factors and mental health diagnoses that have been associated with elevated suicide risk (though sadly, these measures typically do not touch the realm of moral injuries, which I've observed to be a common thread in many self-destructive crises).

We may also have more skill than most people in reading body language. In addition, experienced professionals have internalized an understanding of how people move through pain to recovery. Based on this, we can authentically communicate hope for recovery because we know that therapy can, and does, save lives.

At the same time, there are a number of largely overlooked issues with the professional defender model. In other words, mental health professionals have some serious limitations when it comes to assessing and treating suicide risk. For example, therapeutic relationships, particularly with certain populations, often start as low-trust relationships. In fact, according to recent data collected by the Department of Defense, an active duty service member who is struggling is more likely to turn to a military peer, a friend outside the military, a parent, or a spouse rather than a professional mental health provider.

In a list of twelve potential categories of people that an active duty service member would talk to when feeling stressed or overwhelmed, mental health providers are tenth on the list, just slightly above attorneys.[78] As I have pointed out in earlier chapters, developing trust can take a long time. Until trust is earned, therapists often fail to hear the true story of their patient's hidden pain.

As therapists, we largely base our assessments on what people report, which is directly related to how much they trust us. I have had many, many patients initially withhold information about how dangerously suicidal their thoughts have been at times until they are assured, by observing my behavior over time, that I will not reflexively put them into an inpatient hospital when they do share their suicidal thoughts.

Even when trust has developed, the bonds of attachment in therapeutic relationships are typically not the active ingredient in saving lives. If this sounds odd, ask yourself, do patients who are in crisis fight through despair because of their relationships with their therapists? If this were true, then logically the no-suicide contracts that were formerly used by mental health professionals would have been retained as an effective tool.[79] Or are people in crisis more likely to stay in the fight for their tribe of loved ones — their battle buddies, parents, partners, children, respected mentors, and trusted friends? If the latter, then why do we continue to place the therapeutic relationship at the center of crisis interventions?

Also, might there be a hidden cost in communicating that the only people who are truly safe to hear our deepest pain are behavioral health professionals? What is the cost of leading people to believe that the only time they can reveal the fox in their gut is with someone who is professionally constrained by the terms of their license to maintain confidentiality? Might a therapy relationship actually limit us when it is used to replace our human need to develop and maintain a deep connection with our tribe?

Professional mental health providers (myself included) have some additional limitations. For instance, therapists have very limited visibility in terms of how patients are faring in their day-to-day lives. In the best possible circumstance, we have perhaps fifty minutes in the course of a 168-hour week to visualize a given patient — and this assumes that we have capacity to see patients on a weekly basis, which is impossible in many health-care systems nowadays.

We do not have a window into whether our patients are withdrawing from those they love and trust, whether they are showing up for work or not, and whether there has been a significant increase in their use of drugs and alcohol. We can only experience a person in the context of the therapy relationship. We can't see the quality or depth of their relationships outside of therapy. We don't know their tribe — the people they love and trust who can be deployed to support them in times of struggle. When we consider the things that we *don't know* as professional defenders, from a tactical perspective, it's like fighting a night battle without night-vision goggles.

In fact, loved ones have at least five strategically critical advantages over mental health professionals when it comes to saving lives. For instance, many of the things that professional defenders don't know and can't directly assess are more easily observable by those who live and work with our patients every day. Those who regularly interact with someone are best positioned to observe behavioral changes that may signal a potential state of crisis. Those in a person's inner circle have developed a good understanding of his or her baseline state and may be best able to notice deviations from normal patterns. While some who suffer may go to great lengths to conceal their hidden pain from their loved ones, in most cases, loved ones have an advantage over a professional therapist where observation of critical changes is concerned.

Second, loved ones have the power of touch. Physical touch can drive an awareness of connection into a person's psyche more deeply than verbal exchanges. The touch of someone who is trusted and felt to be safe can help ground us. Research has shown that a hug releases oxytocin (a bonding hormone), lowers blood pressure, and decreases cortisol (a stress-related hormone).[80] In the context of a healthy marriage, the act of holding a partner calms the inner chaos and restores a sense of connection and safety. A loved one can sit next to a person who is suffering, lean into them, put their arm around them. A loved one can offer a prolonged embrace — not something most therapists can, or will, offer.

This felt sense of connection conquers the fundamental lie that fuels the suicidal mode, which is the thought: "I am a failed human, and others would be better off without me." A loved one can say absolutely nothing at all and yet communicate a profound sense of connection with the power of touch.

Along similar lines, loved ones can express their attachment needs directly. Clinicians may feel a form of love within the context of a strong therapeutic alliance. But it would be very odd (and probably unethical) for a therapist to say to a patient, "I love you and I need you, so let's figure out how to walk through this valley together on the basis of the love and trust we share." But this is precisely what a loved one is empowered to say. To some people who are in crisis, these are lifesaving words. And loved ones can deliver these words with direct impact at a critical point in time.

Additionally, loved ones have the power of old stories, the kind that restore lifesaving attachments. There are particular stories with the power to blast into tunnels of despair. These stories reconnect us with our most sacred values. They can restore hope. They can place those who suffer where they rightly belong, as valued and integral members of a tribe. They can renew our sense of identity and purpose in life. Sometimes these stories are irreverent and hilarious. They nonetheless have a profound power to stimulate reconnection with memories that highlight lifesaving attachments.

A good therapist is a repository of stories, but typically, these are sacred stories of pain, struggle, and trauma, not stories about hope and connection. This is something I think we need to work on as therapists, but until we do (and even if we do), loved ones are much more likely to hold the kinds of stories that effectively wage war against despair. This, then, is a fourth tactical advantage: Loved ones can become lifesaving historians.

Finally, loved ones often know the other members of the tribe and have the power to directly orchestrate a tribal response in a time of crisis. One of the beautiful things about a tribal response is that no one individual, including the person who is suffering with suicidal urges, is the solitary holder of either the pain or the hope. There is a collective responsibility for responding to crisis that directly maps onto the ways in which military service members operate as members of military units. When one or more members of the tribe notice the beginning of a downward spiral, they can close ranks against the threat of loss of a brother or sister.

In contrast, a mental health provider does not know who else is in a person's tribe like the other members of the tribe do. When one-on-one professional therapy is the only active strategy for crisis response, this becomes not only a professional defender model, but a solitary defender model as well.

We will never achieve perfect predictability or control. There will always be some individuals who will conceal the fox in their gut. They will suffer in silence despite being surrounded by loved ones and having access to high-quality mental health care. But, if we want to get real traction in the war on despair, we need to draw from all the strategic advantages available to us. This will require a paradigm shift from the professional defender model of care to a communal/tribal response to crisis. An assess-and-refer model puts all of the responsibility on professionals, who have limited power at best.

Additionally, this approach may cut people off from their loved ones. It may increase stigma and lead some people to feel shuffled off or shamed. Instead of placing professional therapists in the role of wizards, saviors, or all-knowing doctors, we might optimize the power of our interventions if we came at this like docs.

Docs become trusted advisors, and extensions of the tribe of those our patients love and trust. As docs, we are successful to the degree that we help patients identify and understand their hidden pain. We are successful to the degree that we help our patients regain hope, power, and purpose in their lives. We are successful to the degree that we facilitate connection to the people and values that our patients hold sacred — the things that have a power greater than despair. *When we connect, we survive.*

UNIVERSAL PRINCIPLES I LEARNED FROM WORKING WITH WARRIORS

1. ***We can often survive unbearable situations if we are part of a functional tribe.***

   The fact that suicide is not a prevalent concern in places like the Korengal Valley speaks to the strength of the attachments between those who serve together. The tribe of those we love and trust can shelter us from the darkness without and within.

2. ***Developing individual resilience does not create the same level of resilience as reconnecting people to their tribe.***

   As a society, we continue to make the mistake of thinking that individual outcomes are mainly a product of individual resilience factors. Perhaps it is tempting to lay the responsibility at the feet of the individual because that gives us more of a sense of perceived control (or lessened personal responsibility). Individual resilience alone is not the model of what the military creates, and it is not what we should emphasize for many who come out of the military. Instead of trying to develop individual resilience, we should work to connect people to their tribe, which offers a powerful protective factor.

3. ***Therapy can save lives, and professional healers can be incredible assets, but relying exclusively on a "get thee to a doctor approach" has some serious limitations.***

   An assess-and-refer model puts all of the responsibility on professionals, who have limited power at best. Effective suicide prevention requires all hands on deck. A message like "You have suicidal thoughts, and you should go to the doctor to get help for your issues" is very different from a message like "Mental health struggles are a normal part of life for all of us. You can turn to both your tribe as well as trusted professional healers to address your hidden pain."

4. ***We may be asking the wrong questions when it comes to helping people who are in suicidal crisis.***

   Warriors, and other groups of people in our society, may not be very self-protective by nature, but may have a very strong protective instinct for other people. Some of us may not be willing to live for ourselves at times, but reactivating our attachment to those who need us may pull us out of a tunnel of despair. Instead of asking "How can we come up with a plan to help you pull yourself out of a crisis?" a better question might be, "How can we help you draw from the strength of your tribe to give you the will to stay in the fight?"

QUESTIONS FOR REFLECTION AND APPLICATION

1. In this chapter, we discussed the power of social support from the tribe of those we love and trust. To apply this, can you think of a time when have you had to draw from the strength of others to reach an important goal? When have others infused you with a strength you didn't know you had? How did it feel when other people loaned you their strength?

2. Those who serve in our military and first responder communities commonly operate according to values they hold sacred. If you had to define the three personal values that are most sacred to you, what would they be? When you behave in ways that violate these values, is the degree of guilt or shame you feel deeper or greater than in other instances of behaviors and choices you regret?

3. Have you ever heard the story of the Japanese American 442nd Infantry Regiment prior to reading this chapter? What thoughts or feelings came up for you in hearing my patient's account? What does his story and the story of the 442nd reveal about the ways in which we as a nation have treated certain groups of citizens? (Learn more by visiting www.GoForBroke.org). What does it do to us as a nation when we violate our most sacred values?

4. Gaining the support of those within our tribe brings emotional benefits. Can you think of a time when the presence, touch, or voice of someone you love and trust has grounded you and made you feel safe during a time of crisis? How can you offer this gift of emotional support to others in your life?

5. Those who serve in our military and first responder populations often have a connection with each other that can be hard to describe in words. Can you think of two or three stories in your life so far

that capture moments of deep connection to others or that help you remember something that is critical to your sense of personal identity? Do you share these stories with others, or do you keep them tucked away in your memory bank?

Check out the handbook at the end of the book for further ways to apply this content.

10

A DIFFERENT KIND OF WAR

On a day just like any other, I started the walk down the hall to pick up my next patient and heard unnatural straining sounds in the office just across from mine. A veteran was in the process of attempting suicide. One of my colleagues was struggling to bear the veteran's weight while another was trying to untie the knot in the cord that was strangling the veteran. Without conscious thought, and with total clarity,[81] I saw that we needed to cut the cord. I owe this insight directly to one of my patients, who had told me how he stopped an attempted suicide of a fellow recruit during boot camp in this way. I joined them, and the three of us together held the veteran's weight while we called to a fourth colleague to cut the cord.

For the rest of the day, several colleagues dropped by my office. With moist eyes, they asked me how I was doing, clearly assuming that I was traumatized by what had happened. When they offered compassion to me, I felt split. Because the truth is that I was totally charged with adrenaline, and I felt better than just fine. Far from being traumatized by the suicide attempt, I felt great. We had been the quick reaction force that that veteran needed that day. By working together and staying calm during this acutely stressful situation, we had saved a life. We had won a battle in the greater war on hopelessness.

I privately felt that I had been directly tested in the battle that is my life's present focus, and that I had acted exactly as I would have hoped. And I wanted to hide my face for fear that my colleagues might judge my emotional response as inappropriate.[82] I then thought about how combat warriors may have similar experiences when we approach them with questions about symptoms and problems, assuming that we know what causes them to feel traumatized based on what might traumatize us.

Of course, if the suicide attempt had resulted in a death that day, that would have changed everything. In that case, I probably would have struggled with the feeling of helplessness that so many of my patients had reported in the wake of a suicide. This is why I started using the term "sniper effect" in sessions where my patients had experienced a suicide loss. The sniper effect put into words the experience of losing a battle buddy suddenly to an unseen, unknown enemy. It captured the feeling that irreplaceable people are getting ambushed and picked off by their demons, leaving a wake of devastation for their loved ones. These experiences inspired me to develop what I call "the tactical analysis of mental warfare," which I'll describe in this chapter.

As long as we keep suicide in the realm of mental health and frame it from a mental health perspective, those who are impacted by these losses will continue to feel helpless. Warriors are people of action. Helplessness is one of the most intolerable feelings for a warrior, and helplessness around the issue of suicide loss was pervasive among my patients. When I put this together, I started to think about the battle to prevent suicide in different terms. Specifically, I asked myself: What would happen if we were to put the battle into tactical warfare terms instead of mental health terms? I had a good framework to draw upon because one of my patients had asked me to read the *Marine Rifle Squad* manual in the past.

As he explained, 'it's not light reading, but it will help you think like a Marine.' Light vacation reading it is not. At more than 350 pages in length, the *Marine Rifle Squad* manual "describes the organization, weapons, capabilities, and limitations of the Marine rifle squad … offensive and defensive tactics and techniques, as well as the different types of patrols the squad will conduct."[83] But he was right. It helped me to better understand the psychology of those who are the "first to fight."

Consider this language, which is pulled from Section 5-8 of the *Marine Rifle Squad* manual: "Having an idea as to what the enemy can do, what weapons he will employ, and what his strength is, will help the squad leader organize his [or her] defense to meet that threat."[84] When I mapped this understanding onto what I was seeing in the aftermath of suicide, I realized that Marines can't adapt and overcome if they have no tactical understanding of the battle they are fighting, and they have no good understanding of what the enemy can do, what weapons he will employ, and what his strength is.

Perhaps this is true for all of us. Without this understanding, our flank is wide open. And as someone who has walked with many warriors at the end of a tunnel of despair, I can provide the tactical analysis that is needed to get traction in what is a different kind of war.

A Tactical Analysis of Mental Warfare

First of all, knowledge of the enemy is the basis for a good plan of attack. So, the enemy must be identified. This enemy is as sly and cunning as a fox. Its attacks are guerrilla warfare of a psychological type. It uses stealth and makes its attacks when people are alone and unarmed. It creates feelings of shame that further separate individuals from the tribe of those who could keep them in the fight.

Warriors often call this enemy their demons, so let's go with that. "Demons" does not necessarily refer to the kind of demons that are described in the Bible, although some do see this as spiritual warfare. For others, "demons" is used as a metaphor for the voice of hopelessness. You can take the word "demons" however you will, depending on your background and personal beliefs.

I asked several of my patients to describe their demons. They were sometimes described as "a voice without a body" that "tells you over and over that you are a worthless shitbag." Interestingly, the source of the voice can shift over time. As many of my patients put it, "At first, the voices are those of other people — telling you that you are a screw-up. But over time, the voice becomes your own voice, telling you that everyone would be much better off without you."

Others described their demons as having a physical form — something "dark and sticky" that infects them over time with hopeless thoughts and feelings. Some described a process where they feel like they "become a monster" over time until they are one with their demons. This is a particularly dangerous shift because often, at this point, the only way they can see to end the threat is to end their life. Even so, when these poisonous thoughts are flushed out in a safe space, with those they trust, the voice of hope has the power to help them stay in the fight.

Now that we have named and described the enemy, we need to develop a good understanding of how the enemy fights, how it moves in battle, what things it targets, what weapons it uses, what gives the enemy victory, and what neutralizes the enemy. Tactically speaking, demons love to ambush a solitary individual; their battle plan is to isolate people in dark tunnels that get progressively narrower and more hopeless over time.

Consider this language, also from the *Marine Rifle Squad* manual: "An isolated unit is easily destroyed by the enemy."[85] The same principle then applies to any isolated individual. So often, we mean well, but what we do actually plays into the enemy's hand.[86] A friend of mine who is a Marine Corps veteran once told me about a time on active duty when a fellow Marine was determined to be at risk for suicide. As he described, this Marine was put on a suicide watch, with his cot moved to the center of all the cots, separated by about ten feet from the circle of cots surrounding him. While no doubt this instruction was well intended, the struggling Marine was immediately separated from the tribe of his fellow Marines, which is likely to enhance feelings of shame and irrelevance.

This visual of separating a person who is suffering and putting them under watchful surveillance echoes the theme of an assess-and-refer approach to handling suicide risk. This is perhaps the most dangerous underlying message of the mental health model of care: the implied suggestion that suicidal thinking is a private, individual battle to be addressed one-on-one with a therapist.

What is intended to be a warm handoff within the culture of mental health providers might actually feel like an identity-threatening cutoff to a person who already feels unworthy. We have had too many good warriors privately feeling like sh-tbags to continue with practices that play into potentially lethal thoughts.

Another issue with the current battle plan — the mental health model that relies on the professional defender model of care — is that we are not taking the fight to the enemy. We are reacting when people are in crisis, rather than creating a culture where the enemy cannot get a toehold in the first place. A proactive approach, based on a tactical analysis, understands that the strategy and mental warfare campaigns of the enemy are *predictable*. They run along these four lines:

> "You are a sh-tbird who is not worthy of the brotherhood."[87]
>
> "If your family really knew you, they'd see that you are a monster."
>
> "You are a danger/liability to those you should be protecting."
>
> "You are worthless/dead weight and a burden to those you love."

The strategy of the enemy is to isolate an individual, to separate them from those they love and trust, those whose love wields a power that is greater than despair. The way this happens echoes the way in which a predatory domestic violence abuser separates their partner from others who could shine light on what is happening. The voice of despair starts with a whisper that creates a feeling of shame.

As shown in Chapter 5, when shame begins to grow, we withdraw or act out in ways that further damage the relationships that give our lives meaning. This is how moral injuries can become weapons of the enemy. Shame leads directly to feelings of unworthiness, irrelevance, and burdensomeness. Shame can also create barriers to engaging authentically with those we love and with the docs who could help us find a path to hope. As the sufferer descends into the tunnel of despair, the walls begin to narrow, and the voice of the demons intensifies, echoing off the walls.

Many who suffer begin to mentally rehearse how they might end their lives at this point in the tunnel. A process of detachment ensues. The sufferer begins to feel the loss of their core being until they feel like a shell of a person. Sometimes, but not always, there are dramatic changes in appearance, and major personality and behavioral changes (irritability, addictions, infidelity, violent outbursts) all of which induce more shame and further convince sufferers that they are beyond help. Many of my patients have reported that they feel "overtaken" or "possessed" by the voice of despair. What once began as a sly little whisper becomes a deafening roar, screaming inside the head of the one who suffers.

And, as I also explained in Chapter 5, the reasons why veterans die are often *not* the same reasons why civilians die by suicide. If we don't understand the underlying psychology that drives veterans to self-destructive ends, we will continue to ask the wrong questions and design our interventions from the wrong understanding.

Here's the thing: Veterans are capable of tolerating a *massive* amount of pain and suffering. Many of the Vietnam veterans I've worked with have suffered without relief for several decades from a combination of ongoing physical pain, chronic insomnia, untreated trauma, an immense burden of unaddressed grief and loss, and a thousand pounds of survivor guilt, but still, they have stayed in the fight.

In many cases, the Achilles' heel of our warriors is not their own suffering. Their weakness is different. To understand the greatest vulnerability of the strongest and bravest citizens in our society, we need to understand the following five factors.

First, *being protectors is core to their identity.* They are protectors of their family, their military tribe, and their country. Second, in their military training, warriors repeatedly learn to take decisive action to eliminate threats. This response to threat becomes ingrained in their muscle memory. Third, they are firearms experts who view a firearm as a tool for eliminating threats to those they are protecting. Fourth, they suffer from injuries that are not well understood by most clinicians — injuries that are even more invisible and insidious than post-traumatic stress. Survivor guilt, moral injuries, shame, and grief are like silent cancers that can put them at risk for suicide.

The final piece of the puzzle then is this: When they see themselves as a threat to the safety, well-being, and hopeful future of those they love, veterans are at heightened risk of moving decisively to eliminate the perceived threat, themselves. In their most desperate moments when they feel like a burden, they become profoundly detached from the people whom they love. They put themselves in the crosshairs, and they drop into a tactical threat elimination mode. Of course, this doesn't explain *all* veteran suicides, but it explains a lot of tragic outcomes.

In the context of these thought campaigns, the warrior ethos can play an important role. Think about how the warrior ethos and the *protective* instinct of our warriors would interact with what their demons tell them when they are in a suicidal mode. The examples below are from three different warriors:

> "I'm a terrible father and husband. I'd be better off locked away in a cell on an uninhabited island so I can't harm anyone."
>
> "I can't be the father or husband I should be. I should just go away so they don't have to suffer with me. I'm becoming the demon or monster that chases me in my thoughts and dreams."
>
> "Your family hates the person you are. You should just leave and never come back. If your family knew what you feel and how you

> think, they would not love you. If your wife knew the real you, she would not let you near the children."

Consider for a moment how the warrior ethos involves self-sacrifice to protect others. When warriors apply this ethos to this kind of mental warfare, they may be uniquely vulnerable to seeing suicide as an honorable act — in a way that resembles the Japanese cultural tradition of hara-kiri (ritual suicide by throwing oneself on one's sword).

In tactical terms, the enemy has infiltrated a warrior's mental defenses to such a degree that the warrior now feels that the enemy is grafted onto him and can only be conquered through an act of self-destruction. This is a major reason among several why warriors, including first responders, have a higher suicide rate relative to the population at large.

In addition, as described in Chapter 5, based on Thomas Joiner's research, warriors are often relatively desensitized to violence and have fewer internal barriers to acting on self-destructive thoughts as compared to most civilians. The really tragic part of this story is that the people who love a warrior — their brothers- and sisters-in-arms, and the loved ones in their home front tribe — are often able, if given the chance, to cancel these feelings of shame.

With their collective voice of hope, they can restore sufferers to their rightful places as a deeply valued members of their tribes. But at the end of the tunnel, so often, those who suffer are cut off from the awareness that suicide *does not leave others better off* — it causes massive collateral damage and ongoing pain for loved ones. Each completed suicide also puts others at higher risk of suicide and contributes to the enemy's goal of making us all feel that we cannot get traction in the war on hopelessness.

Given a good tactical understanding of the war we face, it is then possible to see with clarity the assets we have at hand and the strategies we must deploy to meet this enemy. If we are to get any real traction with this kind of mental warfare, it is critical for us to understand that we have a weapon that is more powerful than despair. Early one morning, at 3:00, as I was looking at the ceiling and mentally reviewing some of my most challenging cases, I had an epiphany that hit me so hard, I had to get out of bed and write it down.

This simple realization has changed everything about how I understand the work of suicide prevention among veterans. And that realization is this: What veterans would die to protect is also what they would *live* to protect. Our tribe has a power that is greater than despair.

How can we apply these insights? When I speak with Marines, I often remind them that while they are some of our country's most capable warfighters, their individual capacity as warriors is not the true genius of Marines. The true genius of our Marines lies in how they fight together in fireteams, coordinating their skills to take out the enemy. While demons will ambush a lone Marine, they can't easily overcome a group of Marines, united in purpose. Warriors who fight this battle with the support of a fireteam of people they love and trust greatly multiply their strength.

I believe this is true for all of us. What if more of us understood that our best protection was in continued interdependence? What if we understood that we all struggle at times, and that when we struggle, our love and trust must be stronger than our fear and pride? What if we understood that the hardest thing to do is the bravest thing: to tell those we trust when we are *not okay* in order to draw from their strength? Here is a quick exercise to highlight this point. In the series of comparisons below, ask yourself which of these two things is the more difficult action to take.

Which Is the Harder Path?

Admitting personal struggles *or*
Keeping the mask on with those you love

Asking for help *or*
Pretending like you don't need help

Seeking treatment in a mental health clinic *or*
Trying to handle things on your own

Being persistent until you link up with a doc *or*
Dropping out of treatment in anger/disgust

There are many advantages of applying the tactical analysis of mental warfare that I just described. Using the model radically reduces the sense of helplessness among warriors I have worked with — a clear description in terms and language they readily grasp clears away the fog of war.

Once they have a target to confront, an enemy that will come at them with a set of predictable behaviors, they get space from their inner turmoil. They start to see their strengths and assets in a different light, and their warrior spirit is mobilized. They come to understand, in their own language, what a public health model of suicide prevention looks like: It's an all-hands-on-deck approach that doesn't just rely on mental health treatment providers. This is empowering for those who suffer, and their loved ones.

As a rule, I have found that once my patients understand how to fight back, they are willing to do what is necessary to get traction in this form of mental warfare. In fact, once the enemy is clearly identified, they often get pissed off when they see how their demons have been attacking them and their fellow warriors in predictable ways. The only thing remaining to do once they have this strategic understanding is to equip them with the practical weaponry to support them.

Partnering with warriors to develop interventions to support them is a natural part of how a doc operates. I have enjoyed a very long, extremely fruitful collaboration with a veteran named Brian Vargas. In Brian's case, I do not need to obscure identifying information, as he has shared the story of our therapeutic relationship and ongoing collaboration on live local television, *NBC Nightly News,* and a wonderful podcast episode called "Shrapnel" that he contributed to NPR's *Snap Judgment.* (If you have about fifteen minutes, I would strongly encourage you to listen to the NPR story where Brian describes the day he wanted to end his life and the lifesaving idea that stopped him when he was single-mindedly bent on self-destruction).

The idea behind what later became the Warrior Box Project started as a mint can that I had in my desk, acquired from my local Starbucks. Brian was struggling with self-destructive thoughts, and I had had an idea that I thought might work. The thought had come at 3:00 a.m. one morning a few weeks prior, after asking myself, "When a patient is bent on self-destruction, is there any tool that might be developed to prevent him or her from attempting suicide?" I handed Brian the mint tin with a key to a firearm lock inside of it. There was a picture on the outside of the box and a picture on the inside of the box, lying over the top of the key.

During that memorable session with Brian, my gut told me to find a better path than getting into a power struggle about his firearm. So, I asked him if he would be willing to lock his firearm and put the key beneath two pictures of people that keep him in the fight — a picture of his wife and one of his Marine brothers. Brian mulled on the idea and came to our next session with an ammo can, which he had already started to fill with sacred objects and pictures. For example, Brian's Warrior Box now contains pictures of his wife, his wife's wedding vows, pictures of his pets, his military dog tags, his contact sheet of his fellow Marines, spent rounds from his time in-country, a crucifix as a symbol of his spiritual beliefs, his Purple Heart medal, and pieces of shrapnel that nearly killed him.

As he relays in the NPR podcast, during a day when he had lost hope, he threw the contents of this ammo can out onto the floor, and his wife's wedding vows and a piece of shrapnel that had been lodged in his body stopped him from ending his life. Interestingly, he admits that at that time, he was somewhat angry that the idea had actually worked.

Tactically speaking, in his most desperate moment, his warrior code had prevented him from submitting to the will of the demons in his mind.

Some months later, Brian asked me if I could transfer him to a different provider so that he could partner with me in developing the concept behind what is now the Warrior Box Project. This was a sacrifice for him because we had built a strong working relationship and had a deep trust. As he explained to me, "I want to develop this with you because I think it can save the lives of many of my brothers and sisters." We did the transfer, and Brian and I entered a period of collaboration.

Our goal has been to build out a "war chest" for fighting demons. The war chest can be any container, but for most veterans, it takes the form of a standard 30- or 50-caliber metal ammo can. Ammo cans have symbolic value for warriors. They have a weight, smell, and a distinctive sound when opened. An ammo can typically has strong positive associations for most warriors. An ammo can has the things inside of it that you need to defend life. Ammo cans are nearly impervious to the elements,[88] so they can be used to store precious objects. They are magnetic, so we use magnetic photo sleeves to give people the option of putting important pictures on the outside and the inside of their Warrior Boxes.

Every Warrior Box is different, but all of them are full of practical tools and objects that have stopping power when they are faced with mental warfare. Brian's contributions as a Marine Corps veteran and social work graduate student have been critical in making the concept translate to the culture and language of those it is designed to serve. Over the past few years, we have built out and refined the contents into a very practical toolkit (which is copyrighted and available for purchase on www.docshaunaspringer.com).

For example, we provide a packing list of ideas for items that might be placed in a Warrior Box. This is modeled on the packing list that is used during active duty to identify the items needed for a full combat load pack. It is a list of the items you need to survive. The life experiences of people are never exactly the same. Likewise, the composition of each person's tribe and the nature of what each warrior holds sacred is unique. Each Warrior Box is therefore adapted to each individual situation. The packing list serves as a general guide that is designed to be tailored to each individual's needs.

We also provide multiple copies of what we call the "Fireteam Accountability Agreement." Brian and I believe that promoting healing and waging war on the suicide loss of warriors requires a tribal response. Each warrior who develops their own Warrior Box assembles their fire-team, the three other people whom they love and trust most deeply. An agreement is made that they will have each other's back in life's peaks and valleys. We developed the Fireteam Accountability Agreement to provide a clear set of expectations for both warriors and those who agree to walk alongside them during any valleys they may need to navigate together.

The Fireteam Accountability Agreement fits precisely with the concept of how a doc can facilitate connection between a patient and those they love and trust. It is a kind of contract, but not one between patients and their providers. It is an agreement between patients and people whom they love and trust to offer mutual protection in all battles. The Fireteam Accountability Agreement puts into words what is at stake, and how the two parties commit to calling on each other in very specific ways.

Rather than relying on one battle buddy, we encourage people to form a fireteam of at least three other people whom they can call on during times of high stress. It is ideal if these people know each other, so they can coordinate their supportive responses. We wrote two versions of the Fireteam Accountability Agreement, one for fellow service members and one for trusted civilians, including family members. Ideally, a fireteam would include individuals from both groups.

The Warrior Box kit also contains a very detailed document that we developed to help people respond when those they love reach out in distress. Entitled "How to Respond to a Call: 10 Ways Fireteam Members

Can Support Each Other," it is a clear, step-by-step method for providing support. There is also a sample letter to a veteran who received a Warrior Box (since veterans have sometimes given each other a Warrior Box with the toolkit and a personal letter to begin with).

In addition, there is an action list to promote post-traumatic growth, and an extensive, well-organized list of resources for warriors and their families. My role in co-developing the tool and the materials in the Warrior Box toolkit also helps promote the understanding that trusted docs can become lifesaving assets and extensions of their fireteams.

During development of the Warrior Box Project, Brian polled a sample of seventy college-enrolled veterans. This poll was mentioned in an earlier chapter on firearm safety conversations, and all of the questions were focused on this topic. There was one question about the potential of a Warrior Box to successfully target impulsive firearm suicides. The vast majority of the sample (more than 75%) felt that a Warrior Box could substantially decrease the number of impulsive firearm suicides among their brothers- and sisters-in-arms.

With the donation of a large supply of ammo cans by Kevin Graves, whose son Joey Graves was killed in action in Iraq,[89] more ammo cans donated by a group of Marines, and seed funding from the Kaiser Permanente Veterans Association and Diablo Valley Veterans Foundation, Brian and I have also been able to provide Warrior Boxes to several groups of veterans, with very promising results. In one group of twenty-three Marines from 2/7, a unit which has been greatly impacted by suicide losses, four out of five felt that it was "very helpful" and "would recommend it to a friend."

Here are some narrative comments veterans have made about the Warrior Box Project:

1. "Dr. Springer and Brian Vargas have brought forward an intervention tool that, unlike so many, is intimately familiar to the culture and life of OIF and OEF veterans. It is powerful, easily accessible, filled with all of the images and their connected emotions that are sometimes the only possible things which can intervene in the horrifically strong cascade and pressure of negative emotions that overtake one's mind and body when post-traumatic stress is in full force. This tool is the perfect positive wedge to shove between veterans and their post-traumatic stress, when it makes the world look like a permanent decision is the only option to stop or escape the pain, during what is really only a temporary event; and save our brothers' and sisters' lives. The Warrior Box needs to become part of the main arsenal in the battle against the plague of suicides affecting the veteran community."

2. "Having to look at pictures of my beautiful daughters every time I unlock my weapons reminds me what I live for. This is a brilliant intervention, and I believe with the right support this idea could change the statistic of twenty a day."

3. "The Warrior Box is on my nightstand … it helps me daily. Putting an emotionally charged barrier between yourself and your means of suicide creates an overwhelming choice to grow (post-traumatic strength and growth). More ammo is important in a fight."

4. "A tool like this can be a candle in the darkest of caves."

UNIVERSAL PRINCIPLES I LEARNED FROM WORKING WITH WARRIORS

1. ***We cannot assume that others will be traumatized by an event that might traumatize us.***

   There are limits to using our own experiences to help us understand the experiences of others. We need to be particularly careful when working with others who have been shaped by experiences that are very different from our own. To come full circle to what I said in the beginning of this book, many of us, including professional clinicians, seem to think that warfighters come back from war traumatized by the violent outcomes they see and the violent actions they take in combat.

   For many of my patients, however, as described in the previous chapters, the hidden pain they carried came from other sources. For instance, five very common sources were moral injuries, past experiences of social rejection upon entering treatment settings, feelings of alienation from their closest family members, private battles with suicidal ideation, and the helpless rage and overwhelming grief of losing fellow veterans to suicide. Without an accurate understanding of the hidden pain that drives hopelessness, we will not be able to get traction in the battle to prevent suicide.

2. ***Knowing the enemy we are facing is half the battle.***

   Without a clear understanding of the challenge at hand, we cannot build a good strategy for action. There are many, many suicide prevention ideas in the world, but without a clear vision, we tend to throw interventions at the wall to see what sticks. The tactical understanding I provided here has helped many veterans get traction with their inner battles. Rather than replacing the mental health model, the tactical model can be used in combination with the existing mental health model.

Docs can become trusted extensions of their patient's fireteams. Using a tactical approach enhances the clarity and power of our interventions. By designing interventions that strategically meet the threats we face, in partnership with those we serve, we can win this battle. The Warrior Box Project is a good example of an intervention that is culturally adapted and grounded in a clear understanding of the battle at hand.

3. ***It is critical to remember that we have powerful weapons in the war on hopelessness.***

   With alarming statistics all around us, endlessly cited in the media, it is critical that we remember that we have very powerful weapons in the war on hopelessness. The legendary courage of our warfighters can be tapped to do the hard thing. As more of our bravest walk point by standing without armor and admitting their struggles, the secrets that can kill will no longer stay secret. Our warriors will be able to lock their shields together and coordinate their efforts to keep the voice of despair from taking their brothers- and sisters-in-arms. They can form fireteams of other veterans and trusted civilians, and agree in advance about what is at stake when a suicide happens and what they will do when they are struggling. They can persist until they link up with docs who can advise and support them in respectful, effective ways. They can create Warrior Boxes full of sacred objects that remind them of who they are, and why they stay in the fight.

4. ***In the war on hopelessness, we can be warriors in our own right.***

   A couple years ago, I would never have said that we can all be warriors. I have too much respect for the function of our warriors to thoughtlessly extend the term beyond the standard definition of "warrior." But two people changed my mind. Steven Pressfield, a Marine Corps veteran and author of many wonderful books, including *Gates of Fire*[90] and *The Warrior Ethos* writes:

> The Warrior Ethos is not, at bottom, a manifestation only of male aggression or of the masculine will to dominance. Its foundation is society wide. It rests on the will and resolve of mothers and wives and daughters — and, in no few instances, of female warriors as well — to defend their children, their home soil and the values of their culture.[91]

The other person who helped changed my mind was a former patient. He was the patient who challenged me most directly (and forcefully) to write this book. He also gave me one of the most precious gifts I have received. During our final session, he gave me a Special Forces challenge coin (he is retired from 5th Special Forces Group) and a letter that said:

> "You have in my opinion, the heart and spirit of a true warrior. I am not talking about a warrior that kills people as in war but one that fights for people in a peaceful way, which in some ways is a much tougher thing to do. It is actually easy to kill someone, once you have the training to know how to do it. It is much harder to work with someone and stick with them through the tough times. To help them learn what works and what doesn't work. To help them overcome the challenges in life. This is what I call a "tender warrior." This is only the second time I have given someone this coin. Please accept this gift in the spirit it was given to you, with my deepest respect."

The concepts behind the Warrior Box Project may have broad application for many who are suffering in silence, isolated with their hidden pain. Like our warriors, we can also draw from our attachments and the values we hold sacred to build meaningful lives. We can do the hard thing and stand without armor with those we love and trust. We can create safe, radically nonjudgmental spaces for others to talk about their hidden pain. We can be warriors in our own right, never backing down, and locking our shields together to keep those we love in the good fight.

At the end of our final session, the patient I mentioned above said these parting words:

> When you write this book, say what needs to be said without pulling punches. I know that you keep your word, so one year from today, I'm going to find you and see where you are in writing the book you promised you would write.

QUESTIONS FOR REFLECTION AND APPLICATION

1. Our reactions are based not only on our temperament, but also the nature of our past experiences. Warriors and first responders may have reactions to various situations that differ from those who do not share the same experiences. As a result, they may feel different from those around them. Can you identify with this feeling? Have you ever felt embarrassed because your reaction to an event did not match what you thought was an "appropriate" reaction? If so, how did you handle this?

2. Times of struggle are part of the human condition, for all of us. During your own dark nights of the soul, does the concept of a "tunnel of despair" fit with your own experience? What additional insights arise from the tactical analysis of mental warfare as described in this chapter?

3. Could creating a Warrior Box be helpful to civilians as well as for those who are warriors in the traditional sense of the word? What modifications would need to be made to make the concept really useful for a different population?

4. Whether you are a veteran or not, if you had a Warrior Box, what would you put into it? What sacred objects would fill your box? What tangible things would connect you with meaning in your life? Whose pictures would go into your Warrior Box? If you were ever to be in severe distress, what and who would have the power to reconnect you to hope?

5. For some of my veteran patients, reaching out to people they trust in moments of crisis has been a critical part of their safety plan. Others have rechanneled their thinking by connecting with sacred tangible objects in their Warrior Box. Do different weapons to fight despair

have different levels of power depending on each individual's history? What role can each play in helping save lives? If you were in crisis, would you tend to reach out to people, or reconnect with sacred objects that remind you of your inherent worth and purpose?

Don't forget to check out the handbook at the end of the book for further ways to apply this content.

AFTERWORD
The Love We Carry

We are never very good at predicting what we are going to feel in the future. In 2016, during a women's retreat, I spoke about wanting to make a bigger impact on the heart-rending tragedy of veteran suicide. Less than a year later, through a string of miraculous events, I was offered the opportunity to do just that, to serve as the Senior Director of Suicide Prevention and Postvention Initiatives for the Tragedy Assistance Program for Survivors (TAPS), an organization I have held in very high respect for a long time.

As I made my departure announcement to colleagues at the VA behavioral health clinic where I worked, I was initially focused on what I would be doing next, filled with hope and excitement for what the next chapter would bring. What I didn't expect was to feel such an impact of grief — the direct result of severing ties with hundreds of veteran patients I had worked with for eight years.

I have lived in nearly every time zone, and whenever I have severed an attachment in the past, I have always been able to find solace in the idea that true friends easily pick up where they left off. My husband and I are blessed to have friends like this, including two very dear friends we hadn't seen in eight years who we stayed with in Australia during my remaining VA vacation leave. Even with very little contact, I've felt able to hold attachments to dear friends like these because there's always the hope of the future reunion.

But it isn't the same with my former patients. In the vast majority of cases, I will never see them again. I have walked alongside them in their most sacred pain and known them through critical times of transition in their lives — marriages, births, and deaths of family members and friends. In most cases, that very private, safe place in my office was the only point of intersection we ever had or could expect to have in the future.

And no matter what they tell you about clinical reserve in graduate school training, if your heart is really in the work, it creates an attachment. It's certainly a unique kind of attachment in that my patients know very little about me and they are not there to serve my needs, but my heart has been fully invested in their growth and recovery. So, there is a strong attachment nonetheless, and one that could not translate into the way I have been able to hold other disrupted attachments.

As I began to sever ties with them, some of them went into crisis and it was a very scary, turbulent time for them and for me. I had nightmares about their struggles, thought about them all the time, worried over them, prayed for them, and struggled with how to let them go.

In the context of this time of suffering, I developed a practice that gave me a good way through. This practice was an adaptation of how I have helped people grieve other types of losses. First, I had to realize that this was indeed grief. Second, I had to acknowledge that grief was the appropriate emotion to feel. Essentially, I needed to get comfortable with the fact that I was experiencing attachment loss as an extension of doing the work with my whole heart, and this was not pathological.

Once these two connections were made, I was able to rely on what I know about healthy grieving. As I have told my patients, a healthy grief journey is one that allows us to remain connected with loved ones we have lost, rather than making it our goal to forget about them and move on. So, in those final poignant sessions with my patients, I locked the memory of their faces and voices in my mind. I listened very closely to everything they said in the context of terminating our therapeutic relationship.

As veterans generally are, they were extremely generous in spirit. Some of them acknowledged that it "really sucked," but without exception, they thanked me and gave me words of encouragement. They told me that they believe in me and that they would always have my back if I ever needed them. So that is where I have placed them in my mind. They are standing right behind me. I can almost hear them because I know what they would say.

For example, a few months into my next job, I was flying to speak to a group of Marines. I had a terrible sinus infection, and the descent in the plane was excruciatingly painful — so much that it brought tears to my eyes from the sheer physical pain. I felt like my head was going to explode or maybe that I would have a stroke or something. But then I heard the faint echo of the voice of one of my former patients saying, "Embrace the suck, Doc" — which is how Marines effectively say, "Lean into the pain, and you will get through it."

When I assemble them as an invisible mental force, I can easily call them to mind. I can continue to hold and carry their stories. I can pray for them as a group, and I do. I can honor them in the next chapter of my life. I can draw from their strength to be bold as I work on their behalf.

I still miss my patients, sometimes acutely, but as in any healthy grief journey, I also can access the happy memories of our conversations, ranging from a collection of hilarious stories to the times when we walked on sacred ground as they talked about their hidden pain. My patients have taught me so much about courage and the bonds of love and trust that make life meaningful. Writing this book has been one way for me to honor this attachment and carry it forward with me on my own journey.

EPILOGUE

I never planned on releasing *WARRIOR* in the middle of a global pandemic. A prolonged world-wide lockdown was not a thought in anyone's mind when I was writing and editing *WARRIOR* for publication.

When COVID-19 first hit America, I was in Los Angeles attending a retreat with about 10 warriors I had known for several years. Airports closed, the support staff at the retreat site abandoned the property, and we had a feeling of being suspended — in a bubble — for a few days before confronting a world that had changed overnight. Despite flight delays and airport closures, everyone made it home. I canceled my flight, rented a car and drove 8 hours up the coast of California with my kids in the back seat, wide eyed to learn that they would not be returning to school.

2020 was a year of trauma.

I did what I tend to do when I feel helpless — I dug in and worked harder than I've ever worked in my life. My husband said that I spent the year "writing like Hamilton" as I completed more than 120 written pieces or interviews in 2020 — for CNN, VICE, NPR, NBC, CBS Radio, *Forbes*, *Business Insider*, *Military Times*, Military.com, The Marines Memorial Club and Association, Gun Talk Radio, *Havok Journal*, THRIVE GLOBAL, Police1, Anxiety.org, *Washington Post*, *Psychology Today*, and countless podcasts, including co-hosting 52 weekly nationally disseminated podcasts in partnership with Military Times.

Like all of us, I felt the strain of being continually restricted in my movements and social opportunities. I received numerous calls from people whose hearts had been broken by loss — whether due to loved ones lost to COVID itself, or to suicide or other causes of death. Our grief this year was both cut off, and continual.

As COVID began to take ahold of us, like many of us, I watched a swell of infections spread across the country. And very quickly it became clear that while I had not written *WARRIOR* with the pandemic in mind, much of what I had learned could be directly applied to help us understand the nature and course of this trauma.

As a bonus for this expanded new edition of *WARRIOR*, I want to help bridge insights in the first edition of *WARRIOR* with the disruptive change and trauma of navigating a global physical (and mental) health crisis. The insights to follow synthesize the run of my thoughts as the pandemic has unfolded.

Shock, Disbelief and Acute Trauma

When COVID first made landfall in America, we went into a collective state of shock. As a rule, anxiety exists in proportion to what we don't know. In the early days, we knew almost nothing, other than the fact that a potentially deadly, invisible virus had been spreading for some time without our awareness.

We wondered, "was that mild cold we had four weeks ago COVID?" or were we still vulnerable, maybe even in the latency phase before the virus would make itself known? Could our loved ones have been exposed? With no knowledge about this new threat, we wanted to pull our loved ones in close and protect them from harm.

Being socially distant was a painful sacrifice. It ran against the grain of our instincts to connect and protect. Within their private places of isolation, people made heartbreaking decisions. Parents had to turn away children who came home from military deployments due to the fear that an invisible virus could be transmitted to an elderly loved one at home. Couples canceled their long-awaited wedding parties. Mothers gave birth quickly and exited hospitals as soon as they could, carrying their babies protectively to the safety of their homes. We did not celebrate those who had toiled to achieve academic degrees, joyful unions of marriage, or the babies that arrived during this period of trauma.

The fear of scarcity overtook us in the early days. For the first time ever for many Americans, it was hard to get certain products at the grocery store — paper goods, meat, and certain kinds of vegetables.

It seemed that overnight, the invisible rules we live by had suddenly shifted. As humans, we need to belong. We need to be around and with each other, particularly during times of crisis. We need to be touched by those we love. Physical touch soothes us and helps us regulate our nervous system. Yet now expressing love meant keeping our distance — offering the hard angle of an elbow instead of a warm and welcoming embrace. COVID was a disease that divided and conquered and took from many of us our ability to feel fully human.

Tunnel Vision and Solitary Confinement

Initial data started to come in. The spread was worse than we had feared. There was a latency of a few days before symptoms would appear, making it much harder to trace the spread of the virus. In some hospitals, respirators were in short supply. During the worst of the surge, those in emergency medical units reported losing up to 30 people a day for several days on end. Mobile morgues sat next to some hospitals during the worst of the surge.

We learned who is most vulnerable — those with pre-existing conditions and those in the late phases of life. We feared for our elderly loved ones while feeling simultaneously grateful that our children might be spared.

But the rules of "vulnerability" didn't always apply. There are many who were young and healthy — to all appearances, in the prime of life. Yet we lost some of these individuals.

With no way to trace or see the virus, we were taught to see everything as a potential threat. Advice columns during this time urged us to spray COVID-killing solutions on everything that came into our homes. Some medical experts even recommended wiping down the endless flow of cardboard boxes from Amazon with germ-killing solutions and letting them sit for a few days before opening them.

We learned to see those around us — our friends and neighbors — as potential disease carriers. We became more anonymous to each other, with most of our faces covered up by our masks. We avoided each other's gaze. Making eye contact became more stressful. The "squinch" of a playful smile is hard to differentiate from the eye narrowing gaze of anger. Instead of stopping to connect, we often moved past each other quickly. We were in and out of grocery stores as quickly as possible. Essential workers risked their lives taking care of us (whether by their choice or due to economic necessity).

We largely stayed in our homes, either by choice or decree. As humans, we are wired to respond to threat, but we were instructed to do nothing — other than sit in our foxholes and hope that the viral wave would pass over us. As a result, we learned that doing nothing at all is often harder than doing something really hard. It runs against our instincts and our need to take a threat on directly. It can leave us feeling helpless and powerless.

Many companies failed with surprising speed. As a result, many among us lost the identities and roles that gave our lives meaning and purpose. Meanwhile, Amazon was hiring.

A New Breed of Warriors Emerges

People lined up in the streets clapping and calling them "heroes" between their shifts in emergency medical units. The same people gave them very wide berth and avoided them like the plague in the grocery store line.

They were the warriors in a new kind of war. These medical professionals and many other essential workers risked their lives to protect and save us when possible.

These new warriors made private sacrifices that were often overlooked. For example, one of the worst feelings for a warrior is helplessness. Medical professionals, especially those in ER and ICU units, are wired like warriors. They are protectors and people of action. They are capable of doing what most people cannot do. They make the kinds of decisions combat medics make in the war zone. More often than not, prior to COVID, with the use of modern technology, they're able to save lives. They have learned to accept some death as part of their jobs. Any given week, they may lose one or two patients, at least prior to COVID.

To lose several patients every single day is a different thing entirely. Being steeped in this kind of helplessness does real damage to the soul.

Many of them also quarantined from their families for many weeks or months while pulling extended shifts at the hospital. They were isolated with their trauma and it battered them day after day as they did their best to save the lives of their patients. They missed their families acutely — like people deployed to a combat zone, but out of their protective instinct, they did not go home. They did not want to risk transmitting the virus to a loved one at home — a child or an elderly parent.

Every day the horrors of their gravely important work unfolded anew. They held the hands of people who died alone, without being celebrated by loved ones in their passage. Many of these were healthy people that were living vibrant lives just days prior to being rushed to the ER and put on a respirator.

And when these new warriors came out of their shifts, we called them "heroes." This honor was well-intended, and they received it with grace. But in truth, when you call someone a "hero" or you continue to point out how "resilient" they are, this adds an extra weight to their shoulders.

It communicates that they are somehow superhuman and that they must always be strong for us.

In coming and going from work, these warriors also saw people congregating together, continuing their lifestyles with no awareness of the horrors that played out in the ER every day. To see people working out or socializing in dense clumps felt like a slap in the face to many of these ER providers. Why could people not understand that their choices directly fed the continual deaths in the ER?

Some people stepped up in support of these new warriors, using their talents and skills in creative ways. The "makers" of America sewed masks. Companies stepped up production and many donated personal protective equipment to these new warriors. These people recognized that a wise society protects those who protect us.

Individual and Collective Rights

In America, individual rights are king. Our way of life is founded on this understanding. And our economy has followed in this channel. Products are increasingly customized to each individual. Website algorithms work to understand the customer as an independent individual, with particular tastes, interests and buying preferences.

It's a "live free or die" America that we find ourselves in. When must our individual rights be laid aside in favor of the good of the group? If a poisonous gas were in the air, and our goal was to stop it from spreading, acting with consistency and uniformity would be the way to do it. To the degree that some leave the doors open, the gas will find a place to move.

Some of us privately thought "I'm young. I'm healthy. I'll take my chances." In the flush of youthful vigor, during a certain developmental stage of life, we have a feeling of invulnerability. For some of us, our personal choices were made based on an assessment of our own odds if we were to contract COVID. Far removed from these calculations was the possibility of second and third order effects. We failed to ask whether we might get a mild case but transmit the virus to somebody who could have a much more serious case.

Those who serve in our military once lived in a "me first" America before they took the oath of service. When they committed themselves to serving in the military, they understood that they would lay their own rights aside for a time for the greater good. This collective ethos becomes a core value for many who serve and for those civilians who are wired in similar ways.

When media stories broke about national guard members sleeping on the floor of a parking garage in Washington, it was not the service members who raised a hue and cry. It was the civilians who witnessed their discomfort — civilians who were speaking from their own value set. The conditions in many deployments are way less comfortable than this. Our protectors make these sacrifices, and usually, their personal discomfort is out of sight, and out of mind.

Do our military service members feel like captives at times, in a system that they don't always agree with? Yes, sometimes. But they soldier on because they hold to the collective value of making sacrifices. And they fight for those to their right and left, and those they love at home.

When they transition out of the military, they enter a society whose values seem directly opposed to their own.

The focus on individual rights and the culture of "self first" is directly the opposite of their most cherished values. What if our newest warriors, those in the ER and the ICU, were to take this attitude? What if they were to decide that risking their lives every day to treat people who are dying just doesn't work well for them and their family? What if they were to quit because this arrangement is clearly not in their favor? What if our inability to properly protect them while they're doing their jobs gave them plenty of reason to walk off the job en masse? Where would that have left us?

At the very beginning of the pandemic, I expressed fear that we may be suffering from a catastrophic level of self-absorption in America. And it became clear that in addition to this, many Americans do not trust the authorities put in place to help us understand how to work together to stop the spread of the virus.

Too many of us refused to change, unwilling to give up our individual rights. And the virus had its way with us, taking several hundred thousand lives.

Work-Life Balance

Due to COVID, many businesses closed this year. The small business community was devastated by the loss of many promising ventures. Many lost their identities, and their livelihood. Many witnessed the end of businesses they had toiled to build. Behind closed doors, the stress level within some of us and among certain families ratcheted up to a boiling point as a result.

Those fortunate enough to retain their jobs experienced a radical change in their working conditions. For some of us, moving our work into our homes was a helpful change. No longer would we be stuck in gridlock traffic for hours a day. We could now multitask during the working day — working while our laundry was tumbling in the dryer.

In some cases, we adapted and found a new rhythm that worked really well for us. Now that we know what we've been missing, perhaps we will never want to go back to the way it was — the daily drain of long commutes.

At the same time, we realized that there are real challenges when work and home are not separated. The lines between home and work are perpetually blurred when one has a 10 second commute. Being sheltered in place for the most part, and working out of our homes, people were able to reach us at all times of day with work related requests. Parents and caregivers had some challenges that others failed to appreciate. Others might say "it must be great to be home with your kids all day long! You must have much more time with them now than you did before as a working parent."

In reality, we experienced next-level parental guilt. If we could explain this to others, we might say something like, "Actually, I see my child suffering from anxiety and needing to feel connected with me. I'm all they have right now. It's not natural for kids to be isolated from physical play and direct contact with their peers. My kids come to me many times a day for the connection they need. And more often than not, I am on a zoom meeting and have to tell them that I cannot attend to them. So, I feel like I'm continuously rejecting them when they need me." Next-level guilt.

Leadership

The real leaders showed themselves this year. Before COVID, it was somewhat harder to discern the real leaders from the ones with positional authority. The real leaders emerged during this time of continual disruptive change.

These leaders continually reflected on the impact of these changes on themselves, on those they led, and on the companies they run. The great leaders among us took a continual inventory of their own internal state and set a culture where their employees felt seen, heard and appreciated. The great leaders among us adapted quickly to the changing climate. They consulted with peers and with those in all ranks of their organization to take the best ideas and move with purpose on opportunities others were missing. They continually modified their plans in an ever-changing business landscape. They adapted and overcame. They shared credit for victories with their teams and made a point to acknowledge those who were most responsible for wins.

The real leaders led us with heart and compassion. They became more human to many of their employees, as they revealed their own struggles, in moments of transparency. They risked the kind of vulnerability that builds trust. They set boundaries on work taking over our lives. They built in time for employee wellness. They were gracious when our work meetings conflicted with the needs of our families. They communicated a compelling mission that motivated those they led. They understood their own "WHY" and used this purpose as an anchor in a perfect storm of stress. They led from the front, with open hearts and the balance that wisdom brings.

A Personal Understanding of Trauma

If there were one "silver lining" to what has unfolded over this past year of trauma, it might be this: trauma is no longer the abstract concept it used to be for many of us. Trauma is not a "veterans' issue." It's not a "first responder issue." Trauma is a human universal — something that visits all of us at some point in our lives.

Americans across the country experienced a level of trauma that is familiar for many of our warfighters and first responders. We now "get it" at a cellular level. We now know what it feels like to be continually hyper-vigilant to an invisible threat. We now know what it feels like to suddenly lose loved ones and to have our grief cut off when we cannot be with them while they are dying. More of us now know what it feels like to lay aside our individual rights for the collective good — to make sustained sacrifices and to deny ourselves what we want.

Times of crisis also hold the potential for paradigm shifts. The urgency of crisis fuels innovation. We now understand that trauma exposure can cause a biological injury. Exposure to trauma can lock us into a state of "Chronic Threat Response" where our fight or flight system is continually activated. Sleepless nights, panic attacks, surges of irritability or anger, hypervigilance, an acute startle response, and difficulties concentrating are the key markers of this mental state. "Chronic Threat Response" is not a formal diagnosis. It's a term I coined to describe the shift towards a new mind state — one in which everything, and everyone, is initially seen as a potential threat.

Our brain scan technology has advanced to the point where we can see the difference between a traumatized brain and a healthy brain. And the good news is that we can directly address the biological injury that is caused by trauma exposure with a number of innovative treatments that are now available.

One of these treatments is called Stellate Ganglion Block (or "SGB"). SGB involves injecting a commonly used anesthetic medication into a bundle of nerves in the neck a few inches above the collarbone. Bathing this bundle of nerves in the anesthetic medication can calm an over-active fight or flight system. SGB does not block emotions or anything else. I have been in the operating room with several of my patients who have had this procedure. They often say things like, "It feels as though a crushing weight has been lifted off my chest", "I feel calm and happy for the first time in many years" or "I got my first night of good sleep in many years."

During this year of trauma, many in my network reached out for this help. I referred several of them to the only clinic launched by Stella at the start of the pandemic, Dr. Eugene Lipov's clinic in Chicago. Out of desperate need for relief, these patients flew to Chicago in the middle of the pandemic. Some were medical warriors working on the front-lines of COVID units. One called after the death of George Floyd to say that he needed help. The racial hatred in our country had become too much when stacked on top of his previous traumas. Our brave medical providers received and treated them. After getting a Stellate Ganglion Block, one of them took a walk around Chicago and sent me a text that said, "I forgot how beautiful the world is when my brain stops telling me that it's trying to kill me."

During this year I received continual confirmation of the theory that combining biological and psychological treatment results in game changing outcomes for patients. When I was first trained in treating trauma, I was taught that the only way through the trauma was to face it directly and sit with it until the overwhelming anxiety decreased. For several years, I helped patients walk into that space and hold their ground while they were emotionally overrun by their mental trauma.

Those who stayed the course of treatment did get better. This aggressive approach to trauma is a good fit for a certain portion of patients. But for many, it never felt right to send them out to drive on the freeways so soon after these sessions. I did as much as I could to help them shift back into a more normal gear, but the body takes time to downshift.

In addition, many of my patients seemed to have lost the ability to downshift. Several of them told me that they 'felt like a muscle car that was always revving and could not throttle down no matter what.' These kinds of statements helped me see that trauma causes a biological injury that is maintained by changes in thinking and behavior.

Asking patients to repeatedly face what they would rather avoid — while they are in a hyper activated state — is very hard on them. Many of them drop out of treatment entirely. During a training course on a form of exposure therapy, within my cohort of four therapists in training, I was the only one to complete the required sessions on time. The three other providers were unable to complete the training requirements because their patients continually dropped out from this form of care.

Some of my patients told me about a new form of therapy called EMDR and urged me to get trained in this. The VA funded my training with a retired colonel who primarily treated military service members and veterans in his practice.

EMDR refers to "Eye Movement Desensitization and Reprocessing." Using bilateral eye movement or other bilateral stimulation helps ground people when they are confronting their traumas. Slow bilateral stimulation can help people regulate their fight or flight system to a certain degree. EMDR does not require patients to share details of their trauma with a provider. For a stretch of time, I was the only provider in my VA clinic that was certified in EMDR. I found it to be an effective, more compassionate means of bringing my patients relief.

I adapted EMDR in several ways to optimize its positive impact. At one time, I was asked to edit a book on EMDR adaptations within certain sub-populations by Springer Press (a well-respected academic publishing company that shares my name but has no relation to me). It would have been a worthy project, but I was too stretched to take it on. Instead of holding these concepts to myself, here are a few examples of the ways that EMDR can be modified to support the patient's healing process.

1. EMDR resourcing protocols can be adapted with imaginal scripts to help patients envision the "tribe" of those they love and trust, especially after they sustain attachment wounds when they are separated from their units after discharge. This is especially powerful when used during military-to-civilian transition and can help Veterans adapt more fully to life's challenges.

2. Future scripting in combination with resourcing protocols can be used to help Veterans mentally rehearse and walk through a variety of challenges they encounter after discharge (i.e., attending a crowded sports event with their families).

3. Bilateral stimulation can be used to facilitate memory-retrieval, which is helpful in productive grieving, especially given that thwarted grief is a huge and often overlooked issue for Veterans, even in healing spaces. Helping patients with memory recall also has other potential therapeutic applications. For instance, I once had a veteran patient who wrote what he felt was his best novel yet, only

to lose the journal in which he had written it. Just as J. K. Rowling wrote the narrative arc for what would be Harry Potter on a pile of napkins, his creativity had burst forth in a sudden flash of inspiration while attending a professional conference. Writing as fast as humanly possible, he pinned down the narrative arc and wrote the first hundred pages. Somehow, he had lost his journal. I'll leave it to the Freudian Psychologists to speculate as to whether this signified a sub-conscious motivation to self-sabotage. What I can say is that this patient's life quest was to write a great American novel. His entire life was grounded in his identity as a writer. He had filled hundreds of those black and white "composition" notebooks over a span of 50 years. As a result, the loss of his work was a substantial trauma for him. To address this, I had him bring a blank composition notebook, the same kind he had lost, into our next session, and used bilateral stimulation while mentally bringing him back to the place where he had written his best work yet. Between processing sets, he feverishly wrote down what he was recalling. Within the first 20 minutes of our time together, his look of utter defeat dissolved before my eyes. The spark of hope returned during that single session and he walked out of my office with renewed vigor.

4. A history of being bullied was a common (and often overlooked) background factor for several Veteran patients on my caseload. Enlisting in the military to become a "bad ass" can be a defensive response to feelings of helplessness related to early life experiences of trauma. In some cases, resourcing protocols to summon protective figures is helpful. This is a standard application of EMDR. What I sometimes did though was to use their present self to mentally go back and rescue their former self. You can then help them integrate this by mapping it into their identity in a way that helps them understand that they can protect themselves now.

5. Termination of therapy is uniquely challenging for many Veterans. Losing their attachment to a trusted "Doc" can be an attachment

wound. A trusted therapist or a peer specialist may be the first person with whom they have risked emotional vulnerability, even if they are living with a supportive spouse. As I've mentioned elsewhere in this book, after 8 years at the VA, when I did detach from my caseload of several hundred patients, it was intensely painful on both sides. I needed a strategy that would protect the attachment we had built. Milton Erickson writes about this beautiful concept of the therapist's "voice going with the patient." When trying to preserve the essence of an important therapeutic attachment, I've discovered that this can be achieved by creating an internalized representation of myself as a permanent part of their mental pit crew (or fireteam). Such is the power of our attachments and our network of internalized representations. Even when our lives take different paths, our voice can go with those we care about. A patient can hold the attachment with their healers, and we can serve as a compassionate guide for future challenges, should this be helpful to them. Once this supportive "voice" is encoded in their memory, they can pull the file at any time, and mentally walk themselves through the kind of conversation we would have had about a certain challenge.

Even though I did my best to use, and optimize, the most advanced treatments available to bring my patients relief, some patients continued to suffer. One was a special forces medic I had worked with for about two years. He had been part of a weekly six-month moral injury group. He had employed an aggressive approach and was a wonderful partner in treatment. He went so far as to get a job at the local hardware store to habituate to his chronic fight or flight symptoms. Still, he continued to suffer. He could not get calm in his own body.

In the last few months of an eight-year tour of duty at the VA, he came to me and asked me if I could get him a Stellate Ganglion Block. SGB has been deployed in several military hospitals. It is a "go to" treatment for trauma within several Special Forces units. Our military has used it to treat operators and combat flight nurses to get them efficient relief and get them back on the line. Elite athletes have also used SGB to regulate their fight or flight system to optimize their performance. Like many psychologists, I had never heard of it.

I did a review of the literature and had a serious conversation with my patient. I told him that "the data was still coming in." I asked him whether he wanted to take a risk on a procedure that had not been extensively researched to treat trauma symptoms (at that time).

He looked at me directly and said this. "Doc, I trust you with my life so I will take your advice. But I think you trust me too. Given my medical background, I know how the body works. I understand the rationale for why this would help treat my symptoms. If there is any way for you to arrange this procedure for me, please do it if you can. I want you to be part of this. Please join me in the operating room if you can figure out a way to get me this treatment."

This conversation was a defining moment for me. My patient was right. He had the medical background to understand the biological rationale for this innovation in care. He was giving me fully informed consent. Even more, he was asking me to do the brave thing and connect him with a treatment I could not offer myself. I was fortunate to have a good rapport and a friendship with the anesthesiologist in the pain clinic at the hospital.

This VA pain physician was trained at Harvard, and he had all the skill that this implies. By nature, he had always been careful and unusually thoughtful as a professional. He had done SGBs several times before for patients with physical pain. And based on the emerging literature, he was willing to treat my patient to see if this procedure could bring him some relief for his continuing trauma symptoms.

I joined both of them in the operating room on the day that my patient received the SGB. I asked the patient's wife to join me just after the procedure was completed. We sat to either side of him as he cried tears of relief and told us that it felt like someone had "just lifted a 1000-lb. weight off his chest." His face softened. Gone were the lines of strain that I had to come to recognize as part of his usual presentation.

Wanting to do no harm, I advised him to go home and rest. He went home and immediately went in search of a picture of a brother in arms who had died in the combat zone. He had locked the picture away for years — unable to look at it without being overrun by grief and trauma.

Now, as he looked at the picture of his friend, his response was totally different. In our next session he told me how he thought, "I miss you my friend, but you are in a better place now." His guts did not form a knot and he was not overcome by helpless rage as he had been in the past. In the weeks that followed, we were able to get an entirely new traction with therapy. Insights I had shared with him before (sometimes repeatedly) finally took root. His relationships with his family members shifted profoundly during this time. He was able to develop new patterns of behavior that changed the entire trajectory of his life for years after that single SGB.

Because it comes out of the pain management tradition, the treatment is called a "block." However, this is a misnomer because effective treatment allows people to access a full range of emotions. As a result, it allows them to be available for a new level of connection with loved ones.

In this new mind state, they are able to integrate new insights and patterns of behavior. I treated four additional patients with SGB and therapy in the final months of my time at the VA. All of them had astounding results. This led me down a path that would fundamentally change my professional identity.

I embraced the realization that a healer who feels their patient can benefit from a treatment they do not offer meaningfully collaborates with providers who do.

I realized that we need to shift the paradigm for trauma care. I saw that if we treat the biological injury caused by trauma exposure, patients are able to fully benefit from talk therapy. Treatments that help patients become calm in their own bodies accelerate and enhance all the work that follows. Therapy and mind-body practices are essential components of a treatment plan. Patients must address the underlying thinking, behaviors and patterns of relating to others if they are to get sustained relief from their trauma symptoms. Talk therapy providers and practitioners in mind body wellness are essential members of a treatment team.

Treatments like SGB and other biological interventions that directly address an overactive fight or flight system should be sequenced before other treatments. Arturo Weber, a Marine in my network, put it this way, "SGB is the primer before the paint." During a podcast interview with Jocko Willink, Dakota Meyer, another outspoken advocate for SGB, said that SGB is like a "flash bang" that gives you time and space to do the work.

SGB opens a window of opportunity for healing. The fusion of biological and psychological treatments is the most essential element of innovative care models. This is the new model for care that we need to embrace if we are to get real traction with our national mental health crisis.

Since October 2020, Stella has scaled up across the country to address the needs of those who suffer from trauma. In a period of less than a year, Stella has placed twenty clinics across the nation, and has opened two clinics in Australia. We are relentlessly committed to a world where no one needlessly suffers from trauma symptoms. Posttraumatic stress does not have to be a life sentence. There are effective treatments, and they are now widely available for those who suffer.

The Power of Connection

When COVID first emerged, I acknowledge that I had an initial belief that once we "flattened the curve" we could go back to living a normal life after a few months of social separation. Coping with COVID-19 has not been a sprint, but rather a marathon, involving long-term sacrifices and changes in how we live and work.

To the degree that we have been socially distanced, many of us have lost connection with our support networks. Unless we have made continual, proactive efforts to stay connected, many of us have become isolated this year. We've lost the spontaneous conversations that happened in the course of a previously normal workday. The incidental contact we had with others in our communities is gone — for instance, running into friends and neighbors while out shopping, or dropping into an unexpected conversation with a friend at our local coffee shop.

If there is one foundational insight that grounds this book, it is this: *When we connect, we survive.*

This year has deprived us of connection and helped us see just how critical it is to surround ourselves with a tribe. In the most extreme conditions, it is the tribe of those we love and trust that has a power greater than despair. Two people who support each other well can take on the world. A team of people who trust each other in business, or in the combat zone, can adapt, and overcome the challenges they face. The power of connection is our strongest defense against mental warfare.

The most gifted mental health providers do not have psychological x-ray vision. To lay the emphasis entirely on "recognizing the signs of suicide" is to miss the fact that many people in our society are effective in compartmentalizing their hidden pain. Our warfighters and first responders are highly trained to do just this. Others will burn for years with a secret shame, afraid to acknowledge it even with those they love and trust. They will be applauded for their "resilience" which will only add further shame when they know that inside they are "on the ropes" in their private battle with their demons.

If our solution for preventing suicide is to train people up to "recognize the signs" and "ask the question" that will not be sufficient to stem the tide of suicide losses across the nation. In fact, if you provide a training like this at the wrong time, or in the wrong way, you could actually increase the risk of suicide.

In the wake of a completed suicide, for many years, our first instinct has been to immediately deploy standard suicide prevention trainings. For someone who just lost an irreplaceable person to suicide, this can greatly increase their sense of responsibility and guilt. My friend and frequent collaborator, Duane France, shared the perfect analogy to explain this: 'Introducing standard suicide prevention trainings in the aftermath of a suicide loss is like introducing training on wearing seatbelts after someone has lost an unbelted loved one in a fatal car crash.'

When someone loses a loved one to suicide, they are already asking themselves agonizing questions about what they missed and why they did not see the signs. Introducing this conversation during this vulnerable period of time is the wrong call. This is why the work of postvention experts at TAPS becomes critical. Best practice postvention is what is needed following a suicide loss.

Rather than saying goodbye and moving on, survivors must be taught to reconnect with the loved one they lost. They must be supported to walk through healthy grief and carry that love forward as they continue to live in honor of their loved one. They must form a new tribe with others who understand their pain. So even in our deepest grief, the power of connection is what heals us.

And when we ourselves walk the valley of mental health battles, we must summon the courage to turn to those we love and trust. Creating a culture of vulnerability in our relationships lays the groundwork for life-saving conversations. Being transparent about our own struggles and promoting the message that mental health battles are a part of life, and universal to us all, is critical. The world can no longer be divided into those who are "at risk" of mental health battles and those who are not. A "patient" means "one who suffers." We are all patients at one time or another.

Times of trauma tear the fabric of trust that binds us. We have a long road ahead to rebuild this trust.

- Authentic connection builds trust.
- Walking through conflict while respecting each other builds trust.
- Risking an appropriate level of vulnerability builds trust.
- Laying aside what we think we know, and "listening eloquently" builds trust.
- Being emotionally safe and available to hear whatever somebody else needs to share, especially when they are deep in grief or trauma, builds trust.
- Stretching to consider how someone else's worldview makes sense — even when our perspective differs substantially — builds trust.
- Acknowledging that others have been subjected to traumas that have been invisible to us for many years builds trust.

These are the hard things that we must do if we want to develop a more perfect union.

The Warrior Spirit

The warrior spirit is much greater than the conventional application to physical combat. A "warrior" is someone who lives by a code — a set of values that help them make decisions between what is right and what is wrong. A warrior is someone who endures challenges and makes personal sacrifice in the service of these values. Courage in one domain does not automatically transfer to courage in another. For many people, it may be harder to risk emotional vulnerability then to put themselves physically in harm's way.

Warriors take risks in the service of their most sacred values. They are protectors by nature. They lead themselves and others through times of trauma and disruptive change. They set an example of how to turn to those they love and trust. They move to dismantle the myth that a certain group of humans are "invulnerable heroes." They live into the full range of their emotions and enjoy love and connection with those in their tribe. They nurture their relationships and learn how to do this more fully when they get blocked. They persist in the face of obstacles and reckon directly with the things that are eating them alive. They teach us a better way than living according to the "me first" rule.

Warriors take many forms. In addition to our fighting forces, and our first responders who face unimaginable traumas in their jobs, there are many other warriors among us. The warrior spirit is strong in military spouses whose lives rotate on the axis of service and self-sacrifice. The warrior spirit is strong in the "docs" who get in the trenches of mental warfare and bring others to a place of healing. The warrior spirit is strong in leaders who lay aside their ego to create relationships of deep trust with those they lead — relationships that transcend rank.

The decades to come will call for the warrior spirit in all of us. The challenges we face to rebuild trust with each other and find healing after years of unaddressed trauma are daunting. But the warrior spirit in us squares our shoulders and accelerates into challenge. It is time to get up and fight.

A MENTAL HEALTHCARE MANIFESTO

2020 was the Year of Trauma — a year that reads like a dystopian movie script with over 20 million confirmed COVID-19 cases, California repeatedly on fire, statewide shelter in place orders across the country, racial trauma, and rioting and looting on our streets.

People across America are now facing a level of emotional trauma that is familiar to many of our nation's warfighters. And if we don't address what is broken in our system of care, countless Americans will be made to feel that post-traumatic stress is a life sentence. Like so many of our veterans, they will be made to feel that they are broken, that their problems are a result of private weakness, rather than biological causes. And like so many that we outwardly call "heroes," they will suffer in silence, being eaten alive by their unaddressed pain.

We can change this. But first we need to agree on what is broken in our systems of care, and in the healing relationships we form.

The insights to follow come from taking a hard look at my own practice. I'm writing this piece as a healer who has felt the burn of shame around areas I needed to change in my own approach. I'm also writing this as an advocate for the army of individuals — both military and civilian — who will not get the care they need unless we make changes.

If we are to get traction in addressing our national mental health crisis, we must shift our mindset in these 10 areas.

This is our collective call to action.

1. ***Meaningful collaboration.***

   The allure of the solitary, heroic healer is very strong in the fields of medicine and mental health. Rather than being solitary "saviors," allied treatment providers must form effective teams, like our teams in special forces medical units. Teams of healers must set their egos aside and align within a new model of care that combines biological, psychological, and mind-body approaches. Healing the mental pain in our collective body will require all-hands-on-deck. Addressing human suffering — whether due to physical or mental health challenges — is ONE MISSION.

2. ***Patient-driven care.***

   Healers have responsibility for their patients, but do not "own" them. A healer sets the optimal conditions for healing — even if that means referring a patient to another provider who can offer an intervention they do not. There is no single "solution" that works for every patient. Read the science, but don't be fooled into thinking that all science is always unbiased. Fear is used in many contexts to motivate people and shape their opinions. Sometimes, where there is "smoke" there is a "smokescreen" as part of an agenda to maintain a status quo that is failing people. Trauma takes away people's power. The way to give it back is to empower patients by offering them a variety of effective treatment options.

3. ***A communal response to mental health crisis.***

   A trusted Doc can be an asset, but therapy cannot replace community. For too long, we have encouraged a "get thee to a doctor" approach to addressing mental suffering. For too long, we have told the loved ones of those who suffer that addressing mental warfare is an "experts only" issue. We need a radical redistribution of responsibility for protecting and preserving mental wellness — a communal response to mental health crises. We all need our Tribe — the people with whom we can remove our emotional armor without fear of judgment. *When we connect, we survive.*

4. ***Proactive care before problems become a crisis.***

The mind in crisis is an altered state of consciousness. Those in crisis often detach from human connection and from balanced thought. At the same time, mental warfare follows predictable patterns. Suicide is an insurgency of the mind. Just as we have had to adapt our military strategies for the conditions of modern warfare, we must adapt our approaches to mental health battles based on this understanding. We must equip all Americans with the insights, strategies, and systems of support that have stopping power when it comes to mental warfare.

5. ***Elimination of mental health stigma.***

Stigma is more lethal to many Americans than pernicious forms of cancer. Those who suffer from PTSD were once told that it is "all in their head." Now we know that it is literally in their head, and visible on a brain scan. By changing the way that people view challenges like post-traumatic stress from a mental illness to an injury, we can eliminate mental health stigma. After healing the brain, it becomes so much easier to change the psychological components of trauma — the thoughts and behaviors that maintain the trauma response.

6. ***TRUST, above all else.***

Without trust, secrets stay secret. Some of these secrets can be lethal. The first story a patient shares is often not the story a healer needs to understand. The first story is often a test of whether a healer can be trusted to hear about deeper pain — the hidden pain we protect from view. The higher calling of a healer is to build deep trust with his or her patients, so that secrets do not metastasize and lead to self-destructive acts. There is a pathway for us to build trust, even if our life experiences are not the same. But it requires humility and a special kind of courage to get there — this is true for patients and healers alike.

7. ***Lived experience must be brought to the table.***

Rather than designing intervention approaches solely based on professional expertise, we must partner with those we aim to support. There is wisdom to be gained from lived experience. Marines I work with often say — "for us, by us." The healing work we do is a partnership. We must walk with those we support in a way that transcends rank or assigned roles. Trust outranks rank. Ego and pride in any relationship limit the extent to which trust can be built. Building deep trust requires us to set aside any "rank" we may have and listen eloquently to the people whose pain has a faint voice.

8. ***Culturally adapted approaches.***

What works for one group does not work for another. Failing to understand the different psychological and cultural influences of various groups guarantees that our interventions will miss the mark. For example, our nation's warfighters are the strongest and bravest of us. At the same time, our warriors have unique strengths and vulnerabilities when confronted with mental warfare. We are losing some of them because of a deep cultural, and trust gap. Too often, we subject them to our fears and our projections. We call them "heroes" or "broken" both of which deny their humanity. Too often, we over-nurture them in unhelpful ways instead of calling to their strength. We do this to civilian patients as well. To improvise and adapt, we must base our approaches on an accurate understanding of the culture of those we serve.

9. ***We are all patients.***

We must end the hidden "class" system in the practice of medicine. Regardless of outside appearances, human suffering is universal.

Our strongest and bravest citizens, our warfighters, and leaders in our society, in both the military and corporate segment, have special vulnerabilities. When it comes to suffering and the need to heal, the world cannot be divided into "those who have needs" and "those who provide care." This hidden class system in the field of mental health is a deterrent to many who would otherwise seek relief. Our current systems of care create roles that establish relative rank, putting patients in a "one-down" position. If we want to be healers, we need to consciously subvert this class system, while holding good boundaries. It's possible to do both.

10. INNOVATE, despite fear and risk aversion.

Millions of Americans are suffering from unaddressed trauma and other mental health challenges due to direct and indirect effects of the global pandemic, physical and sexual violence, warfare, and natural disasters. Those who suffer from trauma deserve the best care we can provide — care that is practical, effective, and informed by modern neuroscience. Innovation requires courage. There is always an element of risk in advancing new ideas. Regardless, we must innovate as if lives depend on it — because they do.

- Dr. Shauna Springer

ACKNOWLEDGMENTS

First, I want to express my gratitude for the unflagging support of my husband Utaka and my children Terran and Téa. I could not do the work I do — or live into my purpose — without the support of my home-front Tribe. You are all my greatest blessing in life.

In addition, there are a few special people who have gone above and beyond to support this book.

Thank you, Jennifer Tracy, for your steady support. Thank you for your generosity in providing me with 3D book images, beautiful marketing materials, and other creative assets to help me reach more people with this effort. These are "extra talents" you bring — in addition to being an inspiring speaker, writer, and leading mental health advocate. I'm proud to collaborate with you to bring many of the insights in this book and in your writing to the people we both serve through our tactical toolkit and the future work we have planned through www.redefineyourmission.com.

Kate Colbert, your friendship and kindness have been so important throughout this process. Thank you for generously sharing your personal and professional insights in support of my work. I'll never forget the way you told me that you show up for the funerals of service members who do not have any family to receive their flag. When you explained to me that you hold these flags so that if anyone in their family looks them up, they will see that someone attended their funeral and would be able to claim the flag for their military loved one, I was deeply touched. THIS is what it looks like to stand with our warriors.

I'm grateful to you, Jamie Mustard, a.k.a. "The Iconist," for your friendship and guidance. Your work as a successful author and speaker, and genius of design inspires me to make my best effort. Thank you for providing perspective and support in ways that have been critical to making this happen. The world is a better place because of the wide range of brilliant work you do, including what you codified in your wonderful book, *The ICONIST*.

Thank you for introducing me in turn to Mark Slotemaker. Thank you, Mark, for your exquisite artistic eye. You and Jamie designed a book cover that moves me to tears and perfectly illustrates my heart in writing *WARRIOR*. As of this printing, I'm informed that the cover you and Jamie designed is being considered for a da Vinci Eye design award. I would love to see you both honored in this way.

I especially want to thank you, Sgt Eddie Wright. I've repeatedly seen how you are held in such high respect among those in the warrior family. You are a talented speaker and writer, and you wrote such a brave and beautiful foreword for this book. Thank you for having my back. I look forward to supporting you as you launch your future projects.

I also want to express my gratitude to you, Major Scott Huesing. I liked your work before we met — your book *Echo in Ramadi* is a powerful, beautifully written account of the "Magnificent Bastards" of 2/4 at the tip of the spear in Ramadi. Thank you for lending me your talent in helping read the foreword of the audiobook for *WARRIOR*. I'm honored to call you a trusted friend.

I'm grateful to you, Jason Roncoroni, for your steady friendship and for giving me my start in writing books to serve the military tribe. I am continually proud of our book, *BEYOND THE MILITARY: A Leader's Handbook for Warrior Reintegration*. It's the kind of work that pockets of people will hopefully continue to discover and find helpful as time unfolds.

Thank you, Michael Sugrue, for your friendship and incredible support through the process of bringing this second edition of *WARRIOR* forward. You are uncommonly brave, and I look forward to finishing the book we'll be bringing out next, *RELENTLESS COURAGE: Winning the Battle Against Frontline Trauma.*

And finally, thank you to all the other veterans in my life who have risked vulnerability with me to help me better understand what needs to change. At the end of the day, your opinions matter the most to me. Writing *WARRIOR* was a way for me to honor your service and sacrifice — I hope that I got it right.

HANDBOOK OF WORKSHEETS AND EXERCISES

WORKSHEETS AND EXERCISES FOR HEALERS

(Who May Also Be Veterans or First Responders)

Some years ago, I developed a measure of emotional safety to help my veteran patients assess the character of people they were dating. A self-directed version of this profile allows us to examine ourselves for qualities that make us approachable for loved ones who may have a fox in their gut. (Hint: You can also use the same questions to help determine whether others in your life are likely to be emotionally safe people.)

Emotional Safety Self-Assessment

A Self-Assessment for Personal Reflection

1. Do I admit to having some weaknesses?
2. Would others say that I am humble?
3. Am I defensive when others tell me that I have hurt or offended them?
4. Do I show that I am trustworthy over time?
5. Do I apologize, but fail to change my behavior?
6. Do I admit it when I have problems?

7. Do I confess when I wrong someone else (e.g., own up to it)?
8. Do I treat others with a lack of empathy?
9. Do I take responsibility for my own life?
10. Do I blame other people for my problems?

Scoring Key

1. Score 1 point for No
2. Score 1 point for No
3. Score 1 point for Yes
4. Score 1 point for No
5. Score 1 point for Yes
6. Score 1 point for No
7. Score 1 point for No
8. Score 1 point for Yes
9. Score 1 point for No
10. Score 1 point for Yes

Adapted by Dr. Shauna Springer, with permission, from material developed by Dr. Henry Cloud and Dr. John Townsend, as described in their book Safe People. *For further information, visit: www.CloudTownsend.com.*

Your Score: Food for Thought ...

2 points or less: Points indicate issues you may need to address in your way of relating to others. So, based on a score of 2 or less, you see yourself as an emotionally safe person. If this is true, then you will generally have healthy, close long-term relationships in your life with several other people. If true, you should also have good potential to form a solid, lasting relationships with others. If you scored points on any questions, especially if your relationship history is more rocky than stable and healthy, note these areas as possible targets for further growth.

3–5 points: A score between 3–5 points should stimulate some pointed self-reflection on how you relate to others. Character is not fixed, and it can be intentionally shaped by an accumulation of small decisions. Deciding that change is important and committing to working on areas where you scored points can result in positive growth over time.

More than 5 points: You are to be commended for taking a hard look at how you relate to others. You have identified several areas for growth. If your perception is accurate, you may have a history of cutoff or strained relationships in multiple domains of your life. You may have difficulties retaining friends and romantic partners. If your goal is to enjoy satisfying, stable relationships, then it will be critical for you to work on making some changes. There is potential for growth in character with committed effort over time. Benjamin Franklin, a known genius and globally well-regarded human being, for example, actively monitored and worked on developing certain character traits such as fairness (treating others the way he wanted to be treated) and humility (keeping his ego in check). He set a goal to work on one of thirteen specific character traits and worked in this manner, rotating through each trait weekly, for more than fifty years.

Doctor or Doc: A Self-Assessment

Note: I originally designed the following measure for professional healers of all types, including licensed providers and peer support specialists. A "doc" as I use the term is about how one walks with warriors, not about educational background or formal licensure. There are many individuals outside of professional healing roles who may also be frontline emotional responders for our nation's warriors. As such, although this measure is geared towards professional healers, it can also be a useful tool for any civilians who want to become more culturally adept at connecting with warriors and understanding the culture of those who serve in the military and first responder communities.

1. Have you read Karl Marlantes's *What It Is Like to Go to War* or Jonathan Shay's *Achilles in Vietnam*? (If you have read either, give yourself 1 point; 2 points if you have read Marlantes's *Matterhorn*.)

2. Have you seen either of Sebastian Junger's war documentaries *Restrepo* or *Korengal,* or have you read Sebastian Junger's book *Tribe*? (Give yourself 1 point if you have read or seen at least one of these; 2 points if you have read or viewed at least 2 of these.)

3. At least once every six months, have you done something for veterans or first responders outside of your work that was NOT required by your job (e.g., volunteered at a stand-down for homeless veterans, volunteered at a veterans' career fair, given a free workshop to veterans or first responders on a weekend)? (Give yourself 1 point if you have; 2 points if your service work exceeds once every six months on average.)

4. At least a few times a year, have you socialized with or worked alongside veterans outside of work? (Give yourself 1 point if you have, and 3 additional points if you have taken orders from a veteran to

accomplish a common mission — e.g., from a veteran leader while on mission with Team Rubicon, for example.)

5. Have you joined a military or veteran service organization (MSO or VSO) that brings veterans and/or their families and civilians together (e.g., as a volunteer for TAPS, which supports those grieving the loss of the military loved one; Team Rubicon, which deploys veterans and civilians on disaster relief missions; or Team RWB, which brings veterans and those who support them into common social activities around athletic events)? (Give yourself 3 points if you are a member of an MSO or VSO.)

6. Are you aware that veterans typically do not use the word "gun" to describe a firearm? (Give yourself 1 point if you knew this without Googling it; give yourself 2 points if you can explain the difference between the terms "weapon" and "firearm" without Googling it.)

7. At least once in your life, have you endeavored to learn about the basics of firearm safety, and have you ever learned how to personally handle a firearm? (Give yourself 1 point if you have done this at least once in your life; 2 points if you have earned a firearm safety certification from a qualified instructor.)

8. Are you able to watch a graphic war movie like *Saving Private Ryan* or *Apocalypse Now* without recoiling? (Give yourself 1 point if you are able to do this.)

9. Would you agree that most of the time, even when service members feel pleasure during combat and even when they feel pleasure during and after acts of violence, this does *not* mean that service members are sociopaths? (Give yourself 1 point if you know that already; give yourself 2 points if you could articulate the qualities that would be necessary in addition for someone to be an actual sociopath.)

10. Are you able to listen to vivid descriptions from veterans of atrocities of war they have participated in and take these into your

understanding without recoiling internally or judging them, but hearing their stories with an understanding heart? (Give yourself 3 points if you are able to offer this level of safety to your patients; 5 points if you can stretch your empathy to see how the My Lai massacre — a mass murder of unarmed South Vietnamese civilians by U.S. troops in 1968 — could have involved nonsociopathic individuals.)

Scoring Guide and Thoughts for Further Reflection

Less than 10 points: You are probably seen more as a doctor by your veteran patients. Becoming a doc may require some substantial changes from the way you operate now. Change is always possible with insight, and the thoughts for further reflection may put you on a path towards becoming a doc.

11–18 points: You are in the middle of the spectrum. Becoming more of a doc to your patients will require making some changes, but you are well on your way. The thoughts offered in the following will hopefully be a support to you in this process.

19–25 points: You are probably seen as a doc by your patients. You are likely able to connect well with those who have served and can build a healthy trust with them in your role as their doc.

How a Doctor Can Become a Doc

Learning through reading is a helpful first step. There are many excellent books you can read if you want to have a better or more nuanced understanding of the culture and experiences of those who have served. Karl Marlantes, Sebastian Junger, Steven Pressfield, and Jonathan Shay are four of my favorite authors, each having written extremely insightful books on the experience of being at war. It is also especially helpful to read books that veterans themselves read, for example, *Gates of Fire* by Steven Pressfield. A recommended reading list is provided in the next section of the handbook.

While reading can help facilitate insight, it is critical that we get out of our armchairs and engage with veterans in less comfortable ways. The questions about joining veterans outside of a clinical role are included for this reason. In my experience, veterans can sense in less than two seconds whether you treat your work as a job or a calling. There are subtle changes in attitude and behavior that shine through when you engage with veterans outside of the narrow provider-to-patient role.

People whose work is a calling spend some of their free time doing things that serve their mission outside of daytime work hours. They may serve as volunteers during veteran stand-downs or other veteran-related causes. While volunteering is one good way to mix it up, it is also important to engage veterans in ways that go beyond the service role. I was first able to experience the sense of being part of the tribe of veterans when I joined veterans as equals as a member of the production crew for *Veterans Voices,* a local television program about the issues veterans face as they transition from service, or when I was in the one-down role and took orders from veteran leaders to accomplish a common mission as a rank-and-file "greyshirt" on a Team Rubicon mission under the command of Team Rubicon leadership.

In my experience, being able to see veterans excel at organizing and mastering a mission, while extending camaraderie to new members, shifted something in me that translated into how I practiced after that point. Organizations like Team Rubicon actively put veterans together with civilians on disaster response operations. Civilians who serve alongside veterans are changed and come to a much better understanding of veterans and the culture of service.

Exercise: Your Current Role (for healers)

Take some time to reflect on the following. You may wish to use a journal or engage in a conversation with someone you trust to help you gain the most benefit from this exercise.

1. How do the majority of your patients address you?
2. What are some ways that licensed providers might express their "rank" in a relationship with a patient?

   (Take time to really observe how you and your colleagues may express rank through the set-up of clinical spaces, the ways patients are engaged in care, the words you use to refer to yourself, the assumptions that drive your approach to practice. What do you notice?)
3. Is your relationship with your patients one in which you 'wear your rank on your chest', whether intended or unintended?
4. Take notice of the relationship you have with any patients who address you as "Doc." What is the quality of this particular relationship? Has this patient opened up to you in a trusting way?

Exercise: Life Experiences (for healers)

Take some time to reflect on the following. You may wish to use a journal or engage in a conversation with someone you trust to help you gain the most benefit from this exercise.

As a civilian who has become a trusted advisor to our nation's warfighters, I am a living example that it is possible to build and hold trust with others, even when our life experiences differ.

1. Do you have life experiences that can help you build trust with those who serve in the military? (If not, it's never too late to get some).
2. What life experiences have you had that took you well outside your comfort zone?
3. When have you had to build trust with a new group of people whose life experiences are generally different from yours?
4. How did you build trust in that situation?

Exercise: Anger and Aggression (for healers)

Take some time to reflect on the following. You may wish to use a journal or engage in a conversation with someone you trust to help you gain the most benefit from this exercise.

As I wrote in *WARRIOR*, veterans and first responders have well developed instincts about the people they interact with in clinical situations. One of the prime areas where many civilian clinicians falter in developing trust with these populations is around their comfort with aggressive instincts. Your ability to get comfortable with your own — and others' — aggressive instincts, may be a critical part of becoming a "Doc" to those you serve. Here is an exercise to get you started.

1. Do you accept aggressive instincts as a normal part of being human?
2. How comfortable are you with your own aggressive impulses?
3. Do you allow yourself to get angry?
4. Do you have a healthy way of expressing your aggressive instincts, such as through artistic pursuits, athletic activities, or martial arts?
5. How do you respond when your patients discuss their aggressive impulses or actions?
6. Do you ever invite your patients to discuss their aggressive instincts or actions with you? If so, how have these conversations impacted your therapeutic relationship (in a positive or negative way)?

Exercise: Values (for healers)

Take some time to reflect on the following. You may wish to use a journal or engage in a conversation with someone you trust to help you gain the most benefit from this exercise.

Veterans and first responders often live by a code that is based on a shared set of values. Getting in touch with your own values and exploring whether and where your values may overlap with those of the veterans and first responders you serve can make therapy a much more meaningful process. Here is an exercise to get you started.

1. Are you in touch with your own core values? If someone were to ask you right now to list the 5 most important values that drive your life, what would you include?
2. Do you share values (honor, courage, commitment, selfless service) in common with those who serve in the military or first responder communities?
3. How did you first form and integrate these values into your identity?
4. How would others in your life be able to see that you hold these core values? (i.e., How do these values show up in your behavior?)

   (If your values don't show up in your behavior, consider going back to question 1 in this exercise and considering whether a given value really is a core value you hold, or just an aspirational value.)

Exercise: Sharing with Patients (for healers)

Take some time to reflect on the following. You may wish to use a journal or engage in a conversation with someone you trust to help you gain the most benefit from this exercise.

In my first book, *MARRIAGE, FOR EQUALS,* I wrote about the process of how we build trust in close relationships. One of the key insights from this line of work is that we build trust by taking a small risk and then watching how someone else responds. In my observation, many people these days pride themselves on "being an open book." Effectively, in some people, this means that they share everything with everyone in a way that is not filtered.

Some of us are not taught that we have a right to reveal ourselves in the way and at the pace that we choose. There is wisdom in pacing what we share about ourselves with the trust that someone else has earned. On the other hand, in graduate school, many of us are taught that sharing anything about ourselves with our patients is "an ethical slippery slope." We may be taught that it is not "good practice" to discuss any of our personal opinions, experiences, or past challenges with our patients.

I believe we have been taught a false dichotomy that is unhelpful to building trust with those we serve. There is a different way for us to work with our patients — one that allows us to be fully human as we walk with those we serve, while maintaining good personal boundaries.

The key to doing this is to:

1. Check our motivation for sharing.

2. Think through any unanticipated impacts of what we share.

3. Understand how to share at an appropriate level of disclosure.

Think about it like this. Each of us has many life stories — some of them are really easy to talk about, and others are more personal. Bring to mind a set of concentric circles, like the cross sections of the earth we all diagrammed during grade school (crust, magma, core...). On the "crust" of the earth, or the outermost concentric circle, are common human experiences — for example, the pleasure we feel from bonding with our dog, the awe we may feel when we are in nature, the challenge of moving to a new town and building connection with a new community.

As we go deeper towards the core of the concentric circles, the level of disclosure becomes more personal, and therefore, riskier. To give a couple examples of mid-level disclosures, we might share something like a personal challenge with maintaining our fitness goals, a struggle with a chronic health condition like diabetes, or a past experience of failing to accomplish something we really wanted to do.

At the innermost level of the concentric circle — the core — are the experiences that are most personal to us. Often, but not always, these are experiences that are either private delights or private traumas.

For example, this might include an experience we had during an intimate moment on our wedding day or the experience of a sexual assault. These disclosures are risky. Putting private delights into words can somehow diminish them at times.

On the other hand, trauma-related experiences we might share can trigger others or change our relationship with someone else. To the degree that this sharing puts the focus on us, and on our struggle, this can be inconsistent with our goal of service to others. At the same time, sharing can be a critical way to build trust with our patients. When I consider disclosure with a patient, I do it thoughtfully, with intention, and good boundaries.

You can use the same process I use to be fully human with your patients.

Here is my process:

1. ASK: What is my motivation for sharing? ("Am I doing this for the patient's benefit, for example, to illustrate a concept, or decrease the shame they are feeling because of their struggle, or am I doing it for my own benefit?")

2. ASK: Could sharing this result in any unintended negative consequences for this particular patient?

3. ASK: Is what I'm sharing on the outer rings of my concentric circle — something that reveals my humanity without re-drawing the lines of support that should flow from me to my patient? (A good way to discern this is to ask yourself: "If someone shared this on social media, very widely, would I feel OK about that?")

4. ASK: How can I share this in a way that joins the patient, or deepens trust and therapeutic rapport?

Exercise: Building Trust Through Dependability (for healers)

Take some time to reflect on the following. You may wish to use a journal or engage in a conversation with someone you trust to help you gain the most benefit from this exercise.

As I've written in *WARRIOR*, and in my other books, trust is a function of the alignment between what we say and what we do.

When it comes to building trust, the small things matter. When I was working as a frontline psychologist at the VA, I discovered that an aspect of our electronic medical record keeping system ("CPRS") can be used to build trust. Within CPRS, there is a function called "clinical reminders." The default reason for this function is to ensure that providers screen for common physical and mental health concerns among their patients on a periodic basis.

However, tools like this in electronic health record systems are flexible and can be used to help us, as healers, to track important dates for our patients. For example, many of my patients experienced "anniversary" dates related to trauma exposures or the death of people they love — either in their biological families, or their military or first responder family.

These anniversary dates of trauma can sneak up on a person and have a severe impact on their functioning. Many of my patients had not made this connection. Rather than allowing the impact of these dates to ambush them, I used "clinical reminders" to set a reminder for myself, as their provider, to check in with them during traumatic times of the year.

Doing this built trust because it showed them that I was proactively looking out for their wellness, even if they hadn't actively engaged in therapy for some time. Getting a call from me at a critical time of the year minimized the negative impact of my patients' anniversary dates. When I worked at TAPS, I discovered that TAPS does something similar — they track what are called "Angel-versaries" at TAPS — the dates when a member of the TAPS family lost their loved one.

Offering proactive support during the most challenging times of the year is a critical way to build and hold trust with those we serve.

1. What tool can you use to track your patients' most challenging times of the year?
2. How can you show proactive support during trauma-associated dates in your patients' lives?
3. How can you work with your patients to help them track and anticipate their most challenging times of the year, so that even if you are no longer working with your patients, these dates will not ambush them?

Exercise: Helping Warriors Grieve After Suicide Loss

Materials needed: 5" x 8" notecard and a pen.

Set-up: This tool is especially powerful when deployed in a group of service members and veterans that trust each other, and trust the facilitator leading this session.

The notecard looks like this:

Warriors and Grief

Instructions: Grief is a valley of suffering that we all walk. We must walk through "the valley" to experience relief from suffering. Try to avoid it, and it will ambush you, repeatedly. This exercise can help clear the fog of mental warfare and help you move through your grief. Write down any insights. We will discuss whatever you want to share after you've had some time to reflect.

1. What emotions are blocking your grief (anger, guilt, shame, fear, etc.)
2. How is your relationship now with the person you lost?
3. If they were here, what would you need to say to them to link up with them again in a healthy way? It is OK to acknowledge this — in words, by writing to them, in prayers.
4. What do you need to be able to grieve — for example, do you need to forgive someone, to acknowledge that you are angry at God, to forgive yourself? (Figuring this out is often the key to releasing you into healing grief).

EXERCISES FOR PATIENTS

(Who May Also Be Professional Healers)

Exercise: Sharing with Providers (for patients)

Take some time to reflect on the following. You may wish to use a journal or engage in a conversation with someone you trust to help you gain the most benefit from this exercise.

Take a look at the exercise entitled "Sharing with patients" (for healers) in the previous section. Note the concept of concentric circles of trust that can help us pace the development of a relationship with someone.

Is over-disclosure in therapy possible? Yes, if it happens before trust has been established. It's possible to feel over-exposed in any relationship. This is true in every human relationship, including a relationship with a professional healer.

A professional healer needs to know the shape of your pain — for example, if you are suffering from symptoms like nightmares, or floods of anxiety or anger, knowing this will help your provider form a good treatment plan. However, you have the right to build trust through a process that feels good to you.

One of the reasons people avoid therapy is that they fear that they will be forced to tell a stranger (even a licensed one) all of their most traumatic experiences before trust has developed.

To repeat, YOU have the RIGHT to develop trust in a way that feels SAFE for you.

To develop trust requires you to take a small risk and see how someone else handles it.

1. What are some things you can comfortably share to see if your provider can be trusted to hear the more vulnerable parts of your story? (List a few in a journal)

2. Which one would you like to start with?

3. How would you like to share this? (Thinking about your approach in advance can give you a greater sense of control when you share it with your provider)

4. How do you hope your provider will respond? What kind of response would allow you to feel comfortable sharing a little bit more?

5. How will you respond if your provider does not receive what you share in a way that feels good? (Based on your relationship, you may try letting him or her know that the response didn't meet your need, or you may decide to try a different provider, depending on the situation).

Exercise: Owning Your Recovery Journey (for patients)

Take some time to reflect on the following. You may wish to use a journal or engage in a conversation with someone you trust to help you gain the most benefit from this exercise.

Trauma takes away your power. The way to restore it is to take full ownership of your recovery journey.

There are forces at play that can make you feel like a passive recipient of whatever treatment plan your provider(s) create for you. Your providers may unintentionally contribute to this in their approach to practice.

1. Do you feel comfortable telling ALL individuals on your physical and mental health care team when a clinical recommendation does not feel right for you?

   (For instance, if your provider recommends a lot of written homework exercises, and you hate writing, are you comfortable speaking up about how this method of healing isn't a good fit for you? Or if your provider recommends trialing you on a medication that you aren't comfortable taking, are you able to say this up front and explain your concerns?)

2. What are YOUR goals for your recovery? (Have you openly communicated these goals to your provider?)

3. When you ask him or her, what does your provider say are the goals for treatment?

   (A good Doc will be happy to answer a question like, "What do you see as the goals for our work together based on what I've shared?" As long as you make this request respectfully, if your provider reacts defensively, or cannot give you a clear answer, note this as a potential issue that could impede your progress in treatment).

4. If your provider's goals do not align with your goals, are they willing and able to "adjust fire?" A therapy intervention must be based on YOUR goals, and what you are willing to accomplish, not on someone else's goals for your life.

5. Are you and your provider on the same page about these guiding goals? (Sometimes your honesty is what helps turn "Doctors" into "Docs" who can help you, and many more of your brothers and sisters in arms)

6. What elements do you feel are essential to your wellness plan? Do you talk about this openly with your provider?

Exercise: Reconnecting with a Fallen Battle Buddy

I developed this exercise to help veterans carry forward the love they have for their fallen. It can be modified to help any of us reconnect with loved ones that we have lost.

1. His or her favorite sport (or sports team) or hobby:
2. His or her favorite food:
3. The quality I admired most about him or her:
4. The funniest memory I have of our time together:
5. A memory I could share with a family member he or she loved who is also missing him or her:
6. A place I can go that reminds me of him or her:
7. A phrase that reminds me of him or her:
8. A physical object that always reminds me of him or her:
9. Something I encounter in the world that immediately makes me think of him or her:
10. A way to honor something he or she cared about (for example, a cause he or she cared about or some unfinished business I could work on in honor of who he or she is to me):
11. How can I incorporate my fallen brother or sister into special events (e.g., Marine Corps birthday)?

RECOMMENDED READING LIST

A Hobbit, A Wardrobe, and a Great War (Joseph Loconte)

About Face: The Odyssey of an American Warrior (David Hackworth and Julie Sherman)

Achilles in Vietnam: Combat Trauma and the Undoing of Character (Jonathan Shay)

American Sniper (Chris Kyle, with Jim Defelice and Scott McEwen)

At Ease: Enjoying the Freedom You Fought For (Rob Campbell)

Back From the Front: Combat Trauma, Love, and Family (Aphrodite Matsakis)

BEYOND THE MILITARY: A Leader's Handbook for Warrior Reintegration (Jason Roncoroni and Shauna Springer)

Call Sign Chaos: Learning to Lead (Jim Mattis and Bing West)

Can't Hurt Me (David Goggins)

Courage After Fire: Coping Strategies for Troops Returning From Iraq and Afghanistan and Their Families (Keith Armstrong, Suzanne Best and Paula Domenici)

Cowboys Over Iraq: Leadership from the Saddle (Jimmy Blackmon)

Down Range: To Iraq and Back (Bridget C. Cantrell and Chuck Dean)

Echo in Ramadi (Scott A. Huesing)

Extreme Ownership: How U.S. Navy SEALs Lead and Win (Jocko Willink and Leif Babin)

From the Deepest Darkness to the Light of Hope: Strategies and Solutions to Build Resiliency While Fighting Anxiety, Depression & PTSD (Jennifer Tracy)

Gates of Fire: An Epic Novel of the Battle of Thermopylae (Steven Pressfield)

Ghosts of the Valley (Sean Tobias Ambriz)

God is Not Here: A Soldier's Struggle with Torture, Trauma, and the Moral Injuries of War (Bill Russell Edmonds)

Hogs in the Shadows: Combat Stories from Marine Snipers in Iraq (Milo Afong)

In Search of the Warrior Spirit: Teaching Awareness Disciplines to the Military (Richard Strozzi-Heckler)

Lone Survivor (Marcus Luttrell with Patrick Robinson)

Matterhorn: A Novel of the Vietnam War (Karl Marlantes)

Mission Transition (Matt Louis)

Moving a Nation to Care: Post-Traumatic Stress Disorder and America's Returning Troops (Ilona Meagher)

Odysseus in America: Combat Trauma and the Trials of Homecoming (Jonathan Shay)

On Killing: The Psychological Cost of Learning to Kill in War and Society (Dave Grossman)

Once a Warrior — Always a Warrior: Navigating the Transition from Combat to Home (Charles W. Hoge)

Outside the Wire: Ten Lessons I've Learned in Everyday Courage (Jason Kander)

Rule Number Two: Lessons I Learned from a Combat Hospital (Heidi Kraft)

Taming the Fire Within: Life After War (Dr. Anna Freund)

Tears of a Warrior: A Family's Story of Combat and Living with PTSD (Janet Seahorn and Anthony Seahorn)

Thank You For My Service (Mat Best)

The Beauty of a Darker Soul: Overcoming Trauma Through the Power of Human Connection (Josh Mantz)

The Odyssey (Homer)

The Theatre of War: What Ancient Tragedies can Teach us Today (Bryan Doerries)

The Things They Carried (Tim O'Brien)

The Warrior Ethos (Steven Pressfield)

Tribe: On Homecoming and Belonging (Sebastian Junger)

Unconventional Warrior: Memoir of a Special Operations Commander in Afghanistan (Walter Morris Herd)

U.S. Army U.S. Marine Corps Counterinsurgency Field Manual (David H. Petraeus and James F. Amos)

War (Sebastian Junger)

War and the Soul: Healing Our Nation's Veterans from Post-traumatic Stress Disorder (Edward Tick)

Warriors and Citizens: American Views of Our Military (Kori Schake and Jim Mattis)

What It Is Like to Go to War (Karl Marlantes)

What Was Asked of Us: An Oral History of the Iraq War by the Soldiers Who Fought It (Trish Wood)

GLOSSARY OF TERMS AND PHRASES THAT WE MAY NEED TO RETHINK

"Committed Suicide"

It may take some time to rout this expression from our common lingo, but let's work towards this goal as soon as possible. At one point in our history, suicide was seen as a crime, and the word "committed" carries this meaning forward. To say that a loved one "committed" suicide also implies that they made a rational decision, but in fact, perception is extremely distorted when an individual is in the suicidal mode.

Most important, saying that someone "committed suicide" is shaming to loved ones and shaming to those who are contemplating suicide. Because of the link between shame and suicide, engaging in any messaging that increases shame can inadvertently increase risk of further losses due to suicide. A better way to talk about suicide loss is simply to say that someone "died by suicide."

Cultural Competence

There has been a strong push for those who work with veterans (especially civilian providers) to become "culturally competent." The problem is that this creates a false dichotomy that suggests that providers with a military service history are by definition "culturally competent" and civilians are not. Providers with a military service history certainly have a leg up on understanding the culture of their own branch of service, but in some cases, this understanding may actually limit their understanding of other service branches' culture.

In other words, no one can possibly be "culturally competent" in all ways, at all times, with all people. A better goal might be to pursue a combination of cultural curiosity and "cultural humility," a term that is now gaining traction. As I said earlier, many veterans have an exceedingly well-developed bullsh-t detector. Faking what we don't understand is the fastest way to break trust and lose connection with a veteran. Engaging with veterans in a culturally curious way and committing ourselves to never faking what we don't know helps build trust.

Empirically Supported Treatment

Why would some veterans be put off by the idea of being offered treatments that are evidence based? Because in practice, this often communicates that there is a menu of two or three treatment choices that are slotted for any given patient. This approach, while efficient from a medical management/systems model of care, nonetheless chafes for many veterans who want to be treated as an individual, not as a number. I am not suggesting that we fail to deploy evidence-based treatments. I think this can be corrected with strategic messaging. When the peer support specialist and I ran new patient briefing groups, we messaged this as follows:

Everything we do in the VA has been studied and tested. You will not be treated like guinea pigs. You may be offered one of several possible courses of treatment that have scientific backing. It is up to you what path you choose, and this includes the possibility of not choosing one of these paths but instead working with a general mental health provider with a solid foundation who practices in a flexible, theory informed way.[92]

Hero/Heroes

I have privately thought of a number of my patients as heroes, but I keep this to myself because my patients have often told me that this concept is a thorny one. Those who have shown incredibly heroic behavior often do not see themselves as heroes. To see themselves as heroes puts them psychologically at some distance from the brothers and sisters they bled with in battle. What they want is to see themselves as part of that brotherhood, not as a superhuman or a different breed of person. The hero concept fits more with civilian values of rugged individualism as a model for success. In the military, individualism is not a virtue; it is a character defect. For instance, the motto of the Marine Corps is "Semper Fidelis" which translates to "Always Faithful." Marines talk about someone who is of an individualistic mindset as someone who is "Semper I" instead of "Semper Fi."

Related to this, many veterans are uncomfortable about being singled out from their unit for special recognition. Take a close look at some of the public ceremonies recognizing an individual veteran for his or her service. Some appear stunned, most appear stoic. Many of them do not smile with their eyes in the classic zygomatic wrinkle that is characteristic of a Duchenne smile, a smile that displays genuine happiness which cannot be faked. Some of them look like they want to exit the scene of their own honoring as soon as possible.

In addition to nonverbal signs of unease, we can pick up on their discomfort in being singled out when they say things like, "I only did what anyone else would have done," or "I just did what I was trained to do, just like anyone else." This is linguistic code for "I don't particularly want to be singled out, and it doesn't make sense to honor me alone, when so many people I love sacrificed equally. We accomplish our victories as a tribe."

Some have told me that receiving medals of distinction has created a rift with their fellow comrades in arms, whether self-imposed from their own feelings of guilt or shame, or due to the feelings of others who feel their own sacrifices were overlooked. In some cases, getting medals of valor actively separates service members from the tribe, which is painful and potentially even psychologically dangerous.

Along these lines, veterans who have received medals of distinction often have an ambivalent relationship with their medals, especially when they are singled out for honors. A fair number of veterans have told me that their medals make them feel guilty and create additional psychological burdens. The guilt appears to be due to a discrepancy in how they see themselves internally and how their image as a hero has been socially recognized. In the worst-case scenarios, this rift between private self-perception and outward acclaim can induce suicidal feelings. It can feed the fox in their gut.

For all of these reasons, instead of using the term "hero," I use terms like "warfighters," "warriors," "veterans," "service members," "first responders," and so on.

Resilient/Resilience

Many veterans privately hate this word. It's a real put off for some of them. I was curious about this, so I explored it with some of my patients. In analyzing what I was hearing, I realized that the root of the problem is this: The word "resilient" brings to mind two states of being that are not desirable — either shame or pride. By definition, someone is resilient until they are not. So, when we talk about resilience, there is the possibility of unintentionally creating a split within a service member who may be very privately struggling with dark and self-destructive thoughts.

People who are on the ropes with their demons at times do not always appear to be so. Sometimes, those who may be at highest risk appear on the outside and to others to be functioning at a high level. On the other hand, if a veteran is thriving, then pointing to his or her "resilience" can bring up a kind of pride that will have two unfortunate effects. First, it may distance that service member from his brother- or sisters-in-arms if he or she begins to emit the kind of pride that makes him or her less approachable.

Also, given that life circumstances change for all of us, if and when that veteran is not doing well at a future point in time, the memory of being called out as "resilient" then serves to further drive that veteran away from the support of others into a kind of solitary mental exile. So, I think we need to be thoughtful about projecting resilience as a goal. I would suggest the alternative goal of encouraging veterans to draw strength, not from their own resilience, but from turning towards the tribe of those they love and trust as they move throughout life.

"Thank you for your service."

It is appropriate to express gratitude for the sacrifice of our service members. Many of us have been guided to use the phrase "thank you for your service" to express our gratitude. As I have worked closely with my patients, I have come to understand that this phrase is a loaded one that meets with mixed reactions by veterans.

Specifically, several veterans have told me that they associate this phrase with a form of universal lip service designed to make the one saying it feel a little better, a little more virtuous, and a little less burdened to make any actual sacrifices of their own — almost as if the acknowledgment were enough. As one veteran explained, it lets people off the hook from offering any real support or making any real sacrifices of their own to support those who have served.

In addition, for some veterans, the phrase "thank you for your service" can trigger suicidal self-loathing. As one of my patients explained, "When people thank me for my service, all I can think about is that I dropped bombs on entire villages of people, including some who I see now were just trapped by those in power in their country."

A better approach might be to say, "I am glad you are home and grateful for your sacrifices. If you ever want to talk, please know that I am here for you." Obviously, don't say this if you aren't prepared to fully honor this intention.

"Twenty to twenty-two veterans die every day."

This phrase is one of the most commonly used phrases among those working in the veteran support space. It is the de facto rationale for any number of suicide prevention programs and initiatives. Some get it wrong, saying that "twenty-two veterans a day are dying" when in fact the most recent data suggests that this number may be closer to twenty suicide deaths.[93]

Having said that, it must be acknowledged that it is hard to get accurate data on suicide as suicide is likely to be underreported. Commonly, people also do not understand that this statistic includes not just veterans, but also active duty military service members. Further, many people are not aware that of the twenty who die per day, nineteen of the twenty are not veterans of the Iraq and Afghanistan wars, but are veterans of earlier generations.[94]

In any case, continually emphasizing the number of veterans who die per day can increase a sense of helplessness and hopelessness among the very people we are trying to serve. Rather than continually citing these kinds of statistics, a better message might be:

> Every person who has given up their individual rights and served in the military — and this absolutely includes families of service members — is an irreplaceable asset to our society. We cannot afford to lose even one who might be saved.

Otherwise, by endlessly repeating statistics in an alarmist way, we may be socially norming further losses. Instead of influencing others to care more deeply about the problem of suicide, we may actually be habituating them to it, and leading them to feel numb or even more apathetic. In addition, someone who is suffering might actually think that suicide is a commonly used way to escape what feels like inescapable pain. This is a dangerous message indeed.

Zero Suicide

There can be no question that the zero suicide initiative is well intended. In spirit, the zero suicide initiative is meant to suggest that any loss of life is unacceptable. Anyone who has lost someone to suicide will agree with this. However, within this phrase is also the implied suggestion that all suicide can be prevented, which is not true. As long as human will and self-determination exist, we will lose some among us to suicide.

When people take this phrase to mean that all suicide is preventable, it can actually increase shame for survivors who have lost loved ones to suicide, who would have done anything in their power to intervene if they could have. It is a good goal to do absolutely everything we can to prevent suicide, but we may need to shift our use of this term for these reasons.

THE WARRIOR BOX PROJECT

The Warrior Box Project is an innovative approach to address the crisis of suicide for those who have served in the military and first responder communities. If we want to get traction in the war on hopelessness, we need all the firepower available to us. We need a fully optimized war chest for fighting against the voice of despair. One of my former patients, Marine Corps veteran Brian Vargas, and I built such a war chest. We call it a Warrior Box.

Brian and I believe that the same bonds of love that drive veterans to risk their lives for the people and values they hold sacred can help them stay in the good fight. The Warrior Box Project gives service members, veterans, and first responders a tangible way to reconnect with what they vowed to protect: the tribe of those they love and trust, and the values that drive a meaningful life. The Warrior Box is one part of a larger strategic plan that works within the cultural values and language common to many who have served in the military and first responder communities.

Learn more by visiting www.docshaunaspringer.com.

ENDNOTES

1. Contrary to what many people believe, "RPG" does not actually stand for "rocket propelled grenade." The abbreviation comes from the Russian phrase for handheld antitank grenade launcher, *ruchnoi protivotankovye granatamyot.*

2. M. A. Reger, D. J. Smolenski, N. A. Skopp, M. J. Metzger-Abamukang, H. K. Kang, T, A. Bullman, S. Perdue, and G. A. Gahm, "Risk of Suicide Among US Military Service Members Following Operation Enduring Freedom or Operation Iraqi Freedom Deployment and Separation From the US Military," *JAMA Psychiatry* 72 (2015), 561–569.

3. S. Pressfield, Gates of Fire (New York: Bantam Books, 1998), 147–148.

4. I am still both idealistic and optimistic, but in a tempered, more informed way than I was ten years ago.

5. This was around 2009. In the current climate, with such a spotlight on access to care, this never would have happened in the system where I worked. Now, when providers leave, their caseload is immediately reassigned to the remaining providers.

6. When I started training psychology interns, I sometimes shared the advantages of mastering "the art of the frump." That is, if you find the right pair of loafers, loose-fitting black pants, and boxy tops, you will never have a wardrobe malfunction, and the small portion of patients who might be so inclined are less likely to sexualize you.

7. U.S. Department of Defense, U.S. Department of Veterans Affairs, U.S. Department of Health and Human Services, *Interagency Task Force Annual Report on Military and Veterans Mental Health* (2016), https://www.mentalhealth.va.gov/docs/ITF_2016_Annual_Report_November_2016.pdf.

8. National Alliance on Mental Illness (NAMI), *Engagement: A New Standard for Mental Health Care* (July 2016), https://www.nami.org/About-NAMI/Publications-Reports/Public-Policy-Reports/Engagement-A-New-Standard-for-Mental-Health-Care/NAMI_Engagement_Web.pdf.

9. *Hidden Brain,* "You 2.0: Rebel with a Cause," National Public Radio, https://www.npr.org/2018/07/23/631524581/you-2-0-rebel-with-a-cause.

10. The fact that over 1,200 women completed my two-hundred-question survey with no monetary incentive shows their willingness to extend trust and their inherent interest in psychological self-examination.

11. The grief of losing the life one always wanted to lead as a career military service member is both substantial and often unaddressed in treatment settings where veterans are seen.

12. C. W. Hoge, C. A. Castro, S. C. Messer, D. McGurk, D. I. Cotting, and R. L. Koffman, "Combat Duty in Iraq and Afghanistan, Mental Health Problems, and Barriers to Care," *New England Journal of Medicine* 351.1 (2004), 13–22.

13. J. D. Acosta, A. Becker, J. L. Cerully, M. P. Fisher, L. T. Martin, R. Vardavas, M. E. Slaughter, and T. L. Schell, *Mental Health Stigma in the Military* (RAND Corporation, 2014), 17–22, http://www.dtic.mil/dtic/tr/fulltext/u2/a610275.pdf.

14. It is not the only way, but therapy with a trusted clinician is one way that a concealed fox in someone's gut can be revealed and removed.

So, when veterans drop out of treatment, they may be more likely to continue to carry a fox in their gut.

15. A. Duckworth, *Grit: The Power of Passion and Perseverance* (New York: Simon and Schuster, 2016).

16. Sebastian Junger, "Why Veterans Miss War," TED Talk, https://www.ted.com/talks/sebastian_junger_why_veterans_miss_war.

17. John Fannin, "Veterans Are Not Broken," *Military Times* (2/4/2018), https://www.militarytimes.com/opinion/commentary/ 2018/02/04/veterans-are-not-broken/.

18. PCL-5 sourced online: https://www.ptsd.va.gov/professional/ assessment/documents/PCL5_Standard_form.PDF.

19. This relates to what I described in a previous chapter as "hidden icebergs" that can cause treatment to grind to a halt before it begins. This tool was a way that I could build trust, by smoking out, and then openly, honestly exploring ambivalence.

20. Approximately 62% (1,218,857) of all separated OEF/OIF/OND veterans have used VA health care since October 1, 2001. U.S. Department of Veteran Affairs, "VA Health Care Utilization by Recent Veterans," https://www.publichealth.va.gov/epidemiology/reports/oefoifond/health-care-utilization/.

21. National Alliance on Mental Illness (NAMI), *Engagement: A New Standard for Mental Health Care.*

22. In my first semester of graduate school training, I remember getting the feedback from a supervisor to "stop sounding like a surfer" in my sessions. This was actually tough feedback because some of the expressions in question were ways I had learned from childhood to show social acceptance in language that felt authentic for me. Reclaiming my sense of humor, reacquiring some SoCal beach language, and learning to speak Marine have been critical in helping

me connect with groups of veterans who voice significant reluctance to engage in clinical services.

23. Estimates vary between 10% and 20% according to the latest data.

24. And police.

25. M. Anestis, "The Time for Change Is Now," 2018 American Association of Suicidology (AAS) conference proceedings.

26. Harvard School of Public Health, "Lethality of Suicide Methods: Case Fatality Rates by Suicide Method, 8 U.S. States, 1989–1997," http://www.hsph.harvard.edu/means-matter/means-matter/ case-fatality/.

27. Some have used the term "impulsivity" to describe this. I do not generally use this term because in most cases, suicide does not come out of the blue; it is the result of a buildup of factors over time that hit a dangerous tipping point, usually in the wake of a ruptured attachment or the threat of such in the case of a shame-inducing event.

28. D. Drum, C. Brownson, B. D. Adryon, and S. Smith, "New Data on the Nature of Suicidal Crises in College Students: Shifting the Paradigm," *Professional Psychology: Research and Practice 40* (2009), 213–222.

29. E. Deisenhammer, C. Ing, R. Strauss, G. Kemmler, H. Hinterhuber, and E. Weiss, "The Duration of the Suicidal Process: How Much Time Is Left for Intervention Between Consideration and Accomplishment of a Suicide Attempt?" *Journal of Clinical Psychiatry 70* (2008), 19–24.

30. V. Pearson, M. Phillips, F. He, and H. Ji, "Attempted Suicide Among Young Rural Women in the People's Republic of China: Possibilities for Prevention," *Suicide & Life-Threatening Behavior 32* (2002), 359–369.

31. M.D. Anestis, "Prior Suicide Attempts Are Less Common in Suicide Decedents Who Died by Firearms Relative to Those Who Died by Other Means," *Journal of Affective Disorders 189* (2016), 106–109.

32. Harvard School of Public Health, "Lethality of Suicide Methods," http://www.hsph.harvard.edu/means-matter/means-matter/case-fatality/.

33. G. Lubin, N. Werbeloff, D. Halperin, M. Shmushkevitch, M. Weiser, and H. Knobler, "Decrease in Suicide Rates After a Change of Policy Reducing Access to Firearms in Adolescents: A Naturalistic Epidemiological Study," *Suicide and Life-Threatening Behavior 40* (2010), 421–424.

34. Thomas Joiner, *Why People Die by Suicide* (Cambridge, MA: Harvard University Press, 2007).

35. R. I. Simon, "Gun Safety Management with Patients at Risk for Suicide," *Suicide and Life-Threatening Behavior 37* (2007), 518–526. As cited by S. Stanley, G. K. Brown, B. Karlin, J. E. Kemp, and H. A. VonBergen, "The Safety Plan Treatment Manual to Reduce Suicide Risk: Veteran Version," U.S. Department of Veterans Affairs (2008), https://www.mentalhealth.va.gov › docs › VA_Safety_planning_manual.

36. Although with policies supported by statements such as "an optimal plan would be to restrict the veterans' access to a highly lethal method by having it safely stored by a designated, responsible person — usually a family member or close friend, or even the police (Simon, 2007)," it should not surprise us if veterans have concerns about clinician-initiated police interventions to remove their firearms.

37. Karl Marlantes, as quoted in Ken Burns and Lynn Novick, *The Vietnam War*, https://www.youtube.com/watch?v=hoWUwFv1-cU.

38. Rorke Denver, personal communication as part of an "Ever Onward" Campfire Session (hosted online and attended by this book's author on May 6, 2018).

39. Glock is a firearm manufacturer. Any other common designation for a personal firearm could just as easily substitute — "9 mill," ".45," or "tack driver," for instance.

40. A "firearm" is simply a tool, whereas a "weapon" implies hostile or combative intent. You would take your firearm to a shooting range, and you would use your weapon to defend your home or your country.

41. B. T. Litz, N. Stein, E. Delaney, L. Lebowitz, W. P. Nash, C. Silva, and S. Maguen, "Moral Injury and Moral Repair in War Veterans: A Preliminary Model and Intervention Strategy," *Clinical Psychology Review 29* (2009), 695–706.

42. A variant of this would be a medic who is unable to save the life of a service member or an innocent civilian.

43. To include first responders as well as those who have served in the military.

44. At the 2018 AAS conference, Dr. Joseph Franklin described the term "situated conceptualization" to help understand the causes of suicide within various groups of people who share a common set of values. This, then, is the "situated conceptualization" I derived from years of working with veterans who had suicidal ideation.

45. U.S. Department of Veterans Affairs, "Suicide and PTSD." Accessed 1/6/20, https://www.ptsd.va.gov/understand/related/suicide_ptsd.asp.

46. T. Joiner, *Why People Die by Suicide,* (Cambridge, MA: Harvard University Press, 2005).

47. This was true even after PTSD clinical teams were hired in the clinic where I worked. Hiring a team of specialty providers resulted in almost no relief from the exceedingly large number of patients assigned to general mental health providers. In fact, as a trend, many of the most treatment-motivated, less complex cases were assigned to specialty teams, while the general mental health providers were by default assigned to work with everyone else. One of my favorite clinic managers recognized the total inequity of workloads in a creative way, by giving the small team of general mental health providers a coffee mug that reads, "The Few, the Proud. The GMH Staff."

48. Jonathan Shay, *Achilles in Vietnam: Combat Trauma and the Undoing of Character* (New York: Scribner, 1994), 187.

49. B. Duncan, D. Miller, B. Wampold, and M. Hubble, *The Heart and Soul of Change*, 2nd ed.(Washington, DC: American Psychological Association, 2010).

50. I. Yalom, *The Theory and Practice of Group Psychotherapy* (New York: Basic Books, 1995).

51. 5.56 mm rounds

52. J. W. Pennebaker and J. M. Smyth, *Opening Up by Writing It Down: How Expressive Writing Improves Health and Eases Emotional Pain* (New York: Guilford Press, 2016).

53. "Rucking" is walking several miles over varied terrain (also called "humping") while carrying a heavy rucksack.

54. K. Marlantes, *What It Is Like to Go to War* (New York: Grove Press, 2011), 232.

55. For example, pervasive neglect during early childhood is not a discrete event, but it is traumatic nonetheless.

56. Centers for Disease Control and Prevention, "Suicide Rates Rising Across the U.S.," https://www.cdc.gov/media/releases/2018/p0607-suicide-prevention.html.

57. The impact of grief is universal; it can escalate risk of suicidal thoughts for both veterans and civilians alike.

58. Sebastian Junger, *Tribe: On Homecoming and Belonging* (New York: Hachette, 2016), 82.

59. J. Shay, *Achilles in Vietnam*, 73.

60. I use the word "demons" here to stay with the terminology that is commonly used by veterans.

61. U.S. Department of Veteran Affairs, *Suicide Among Veterans and Other Americans, 2001–2014* (2016), https://www.mentalhealth.va.gov/docs/2016suicidedatareport.pdf.

62. J. Cerel, M. Brown, M. Maple, M. Singleton, J. van de Venne, M. Moore, and C. Flaherty, "How Many People Are Exposed to Suicide? Not Six." *Suicide and Life-Threatening Behavior 49* (2018), 10.

63. K. Schake and J. Mattis, *Warriors and Citizens: American Views of Our Military* (Stanford, CA: Hoover Institution Press, 2016), 9.

64. Sue Johnson, "Where Does Love Go Wrong?" Author website, http://www.drsuejohnson.com/where-does-love-go-wrong/.

65. Muzafer Sherif, O. J. Harvey, B. Jack White, William R. Hood, and Carolyn W. Sherif, *Intergroup Conflict and Cooperation: The Robbers Cave Experiment* (Norman: University of Oklahoma Book Exchange, 1961; reprint ed., Middletwon, CT: Wesleyan University Press, 1988).

66. Muzafer Sherif, "Superordinate Goals in the Reduction of Intergroup Conflict," *American Journal of Sociology 63* (1958), 349–356.

67. This language varies somewhat within each branch of service; each branch has its own "dialect," but much of military jargon is common across all branches of service.

68. There may be an underappreciated risk of marital disillusionment for military couples who have been together a long space of time who have been separated for much of the relationship due to deployments. This can extend the cocaine rush phase of a relationship insofar as perceptions of the other person are based on fantasies, rather than solid information about who they are; this works both ways and for both partners.

69. P. Koren, K. Carlton, and D. Shaw, "Marital Conflict: Relations Among Behaviors, Outcomes, and Distress," *Journal of Consulting and Clinical Psychology 48* (1980), 460–468.

70. I have a few I can suggest, including "You know what bothers me about your mother?"

71. S. Junger, *Tribe*, Introduction, xvii.

72. J. Shay, *Achilles in Vietnam*, 77–79.

73. K. Marlantes, *What It Is Like to Go to War*, 96.

74. In fact, one of the stories behind the story was that in some cases, wives were the much more violent partner. I had several cases where veterans were battered by their wives. Often, they were terrified to respond because they were afraid of very seriously hurting their partners.

75. Sometimes referred to as "OSMEAC" with the additional of "O" for "orientation."

76. L. Neff and B. Karney, "To Know You Is to Love You: The Implications of Global Adoration and Specific Accuracy for Marital Relationships,"

Journal of Personality and Social Psychology 88: 480–497. 10.1037/0022-3514.88.3.480.

77. Reger, et al., "Risk of Suicide Among U.S. Military Service Members Following Operation Enduring Freedom or Operation Iraqi Freedom Deployment and Separation from the U.S. Military," *JAMA Psychiatry 72* (2015), 561–569.

78. Defense Manpower Data Center (DMDC) Research, Surveys, and Statistics Center (RSSC), *Status of Forces Surveys of Active Duty Members* (2013 & 2014 SOFS-A), https://download.militaryone-source.mil/12038/MOS/Reports/SOFS-A_Briefing_20160311.pdf.

79. M. D. Rudd, M. Mandrusiak, and T. E. Joiner Jr., "The Case Against No-Suicide Contracts: The Commitment to Treatment Statement as a Practice Alternative," *Journal of Clinical Psychology 62.2* (2006), 243–251.

80. Norine Dworkin-McDaniel, "Touching Makes You Healthier," Health.com (1/5/2011), http://www.cnn.com/2011/HEALTH/ 01/05/ touching.makes.you.healthier.health/.

81. My veteran patients and friends have often been a source of new insights — sometimes even life-saving insights, as in this case. Walking with them on their healing journeys has been one of the greatest blessings of my life.

82. Years after this happened, a veteran (who was not my patient) gave me a piece of his writing. I read it and immediately recognized what he was feeling. As he put it,"What the f-ck just happened? I did my f-cking job. That's what just happened. That was f-cking awesome. Saved lives today. Why am I not tired? I have been up for nine-teen hours."

83. Department of the Navy, MCWP 3-11.2, foreword, *Marine Rifle Squad,* https://www.marines.mil/Portals/1/Publications/MCWP%203-11.2%20Marine%20Rifle%20Squad.pdf.

84. Department of the Navy, MCWP 3-11.2, Section 5.8, i., "Knowledge of the Enemy," *Marine Rifle Squad,* https://www.marines.mil/Portals/1/Publications/MCWP%203-11.2%20 Marine%20Rifle%20 Squad.pdf.

85. Department of the Navy, MCWP 3-11.2, Section 5.8, f., "Mutual Support," *Marine Rifle Squad*, https://www.marines.mil/Portals/1/Publications/MCWP%203-11.2%20Marine%20Rifle %20Squad.pdf.

86. Other ways of playing into the enemy's hand include spreading messages that associate suicide with anything positive or desirable (e.g., songs that glorify dying at a young age, clothing or gear that promotes a link between suicide and being a warrior).

87. I use the term "brotherhood" in a gender-neutral way to refer to both male and female warriors.

88. If you have ever tried geocaching, you will find that objects are often stored in the wild inside of ammo cans for this very reason.

89. With gratitude to Kevin Graves, who made this donation in honor of his son Joey Graves, who was killed when his convoy came under enemy fire in Baghdad on July 25, 2006.

90. S. Pressfield, *Gates of Fire.*

91. Steven Pressfield, *The Warrior Ethos* (New York: Black Irish Entertainment Publications, 2011), 6.

92. The fact that so many veterans chose a flexible treatment approach was one factor of several that contributed to the disproportionate caseloads of general mental health providers relative to those in specialty clinics targeting PTS or TBI.

93. U.S. Department of Veteran Affairs, *Suicide Among Veterans and Other Americans, 2001–2014* (2016), https://www.mentalhealth.va.gov/docs/2016suicidedatareport.pdf. Estimates of suicide rates are estimates in the strongest sense of the word. Because suicide is often underreported, it is uniquely challenging to get an accurate read on the state of reality.

94. U.S. Department of Veteran Affairs, *Suicide Among Veterans and Other Americans, 2001–2014* (2016), https://www.mentalhealth.va.gov/docs/2016suicidedatareport.pdf.

PREVIEW OF *BEYOND THE MILITARY*

Check out Doc Springer's previous book with co-author Jason Roncoroni!

BEYOND THE MILITARY: A Leader's Handbook for Warrior Reintegration

The greatest show of gratitude we can offer veterans is the power and clarity to step confidently into a meaningful opportunity and the quality of life they deserve.

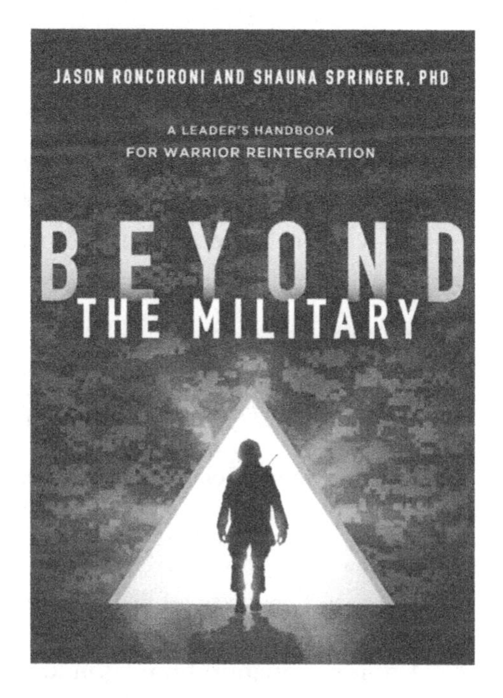

BEYOND THE MILITARY is a comprehensive, interactive resource that addresses the deeper psychological, cultural, and relational aspects of modern warrior reintegration. The purpose of this handbook is to create an integrative strategy for civilian reintegration, continued growth, and lifelong success as a veteran leader in civilian society. Integral to this is guidance to help service members and veterans forge stronger, healthier bonds with the people they care most about through transition and reintegration.

FIVE things that set our work apart from everything that has come before…

- **Confronts the Identity Crisis:** Before veterans figure out what they might do in their next career, they need to discover who they are going to be when they can't be the warrior anymore. The Identity Crisis is the greatest challenge of transition and reintegration, and this handbook includes an 11-Step process for Identity Analysis using the military decision-making process to help veterans uncover their unique identity story and intrinsic potential in life after the military.

- **A game-changing approach:** Unlike other books, which focus on the military-to-civilian career transition, we provide a comprehensive, interactive resource that addresses the deeper psychological, cultural, and relational aspects of modern warrior reintegration. Through the Military Transition and Reintegration Process, veterans develop strategies for optimizing whole health and wellness, social reintegration, cultural assimilation, economic stability, long-term professional development, and close relationship and family adjustment.

- **Doc Springer's Relationship Expertise:** Included in *BEYOND THE MILITARY* are 80+ pages and original exercises written by Doc Shauna Springer on how to navigate close relationship challenges during military transition and beyond

- **A unique collaboration:** Jason Roncoroni, an executive coach, combat veteran, and former battalion commander, partners with Dr. Shauna "Doc" Springer, a psychologist and relationship expert, to deliver their lived experience and clinical expertise.

- **Easy to apply:** We wrote this in a way that speaks directly to the reader, with the tone and intimacy of a coaching partnership or relationship counseling. There are *more than 30 completely original, innovative exercises* to help readers apply the insights they gain. These are not found in any other books on transition.

Military transition is not about finding a new job — it is about discovering the full potential of your life. This handbook challenges military leaders to consider the possibility that their best days as a leader are not behind them — but lie ahead in life beyond the military.

Available on Amazon now!

PREVIEW OF DOC SPRINGER'S NEXT BOOK WITH MICHAEL SUGRUE

Check out Doc Springer's upcoming book with retired police sergeant Michael Sugrue!

Michael Sugrue and Doc Springer have teamed up to bring forward a book on how to win the battle against frontline trauma. The book, which is based on the true story of Michael Sugrue, is tentatively titled, *RELENTLESS COURAGE: Winning the Battle Against Frontline Trauma.* For this book, Doc Springer interviews Michael and writes the chapters to bring forward his story, in vivid color and with all the emotions he felt in the present moment — as he faced multiple traumas in the line of duty, including the traumatic aftermath of having to take a life as part of his job, which led to a time of crisis, and eventually, a path to healing. Doc Springer contributes content to each chapter in the book to reflect on the deeper truths exposed by Michael's story of trauma and recovery, and to deliver life-altering insights in her uniquely perceptive way.

Here is a preview of the content to come…

An excerpt from *RELENTLESS COURAGE: Winning the Battle Against Frontline Trauma…*

From Michael Sugrue's Story

Just after the shooting, I called my wife to say, "Something just happened. I'm fine. But I will be home much later than usual." That was all I was allowed to say. I called her because I didn't want her to worry about me.

Privately, I felt like I was suddenly living in a bad nightmare. But I couldn't communicate any of this at the time. At the time, I was in disbelief and shock. How could this have happened? Not in the city where I work. This never happens. There hadn't been a shooting in my city in 12 or 14 years.

Anytime there is an officer-involved shooting, there are two simultaneous investigations that happen as a result — one led by Internal Affairs (IA) within the police department, and an external investigation that is run through the District Attorney's office.

For those outside the LEO community, the IA investigation is like a root cause analysis within a healthcare or corporate setting. The big question for the IA investigation is whether any of the involved officers violated any policies or procedures. For example, was the use of force called for and used according to correct practice and policy? In an IA investigation, officers are legally required to answer all questions they are asked. They have no right to "plead the fifth." Giving up this right is standard practice in the police community.

An IA investigation can get you fired while a District Attorney (DA) investigation — which happens outside of the police department — can get you put in prison.

* * *

When the ballistics reports came in, it was determined that only me and the other male officer were involved in firing the rounds that killed the assailant. So, really the focus was us, not the other two officers, and the burden of defense was to show that lethal force had been justified.

In this kind of a pressure cooker situation, details matter. Lawyers look to exploit any differences in what people remember and what they later learn to be true.

For example, just after the night of the shooting, I was asked about why the front door of the residence had been damaged. I had no memory of why that would be the case, so I simply said, "I don't know."

A few days later, when I had gotten some sleep, I woke up one night at 3 a.m. in a cold sweat, with a vision of myself kicking at the front door, trying to get in. I called my lawyer first thing the next morning, my heart pounding the whole time. I was really worried that since I didn't initially remember kicking at the door, I would be in serious trouble when it came out — and no one would take my word on anything I might say to defend myself.

Same thing with my memory of who was standing next to me, as we both simultaneously fired our weapons to neutralize the threat coming at us. I thought that it was the female police officer that first arrived at the scene. I had no idea that she had retreated and that another officer, one of our back up responders, had been the one standing right next to me. I had no idea.

Here is the important thing to understand. It was alarming to me that I had no recall of some things (like trying to kick in the door) and my memory of other things, including who was standing right next to me, were not accurate. I was so focused on the butcher knife that everything else was a blur.

In police work, our memories are the basis of our reports. We develop very keen memories of details as a result. Normally, I remember things in detail, and very accurately. I know this because other officers independently corroborate the same set of observations. It was a new thing for me to not have good recall of a situation.

I was terrified that what I couldn't remember might cause me to lose everything — to be labeled a cold-blooded killer, instead of a police officer working to protect everyone on the scene from an armed assailant. I had frequent nightmares about losing everything — going to prison for homicide and losing my family as a result — all because I couldn't remember every detail from the night of the shooting with the accuracy I was used to.

Doc Springer's Reflection

For this particular reflection, I have to step aside from being purely an objective observer, in order to back Michael up in some of his observations about how memories can be distorted because of a traumatic event.

Some of my understanding comes from objective research — for instance, as a psychologist, I'm well familiar with the work of researchers who have shown us just how inaccurate "eyewitness" testimonies can be. In fact, one of the leading researchers in this space is Dr. Gary Wells, who I knew during my time at Iowa State University. One of his graduate students was even my roommate one year. In 2003, Gary and Elizabeth wrote a paper to assert that mistaken eyewitness identification has been the single largest factor contributing to the wrongful conviction of innocent people.

But, as we all know, it's one thing to know something in theory, and another to experience it on a personal level. I know personally what it's like to lose chunks of memory because of a trauma.

And a recent conversation with my sister revealed how holes in our memory can persist over decades.

During my undergraduate years at Harvard, as an athletic young woman, I had a false sense of my invulnerability. In those days, it was normal for me to walk over and arrive alone at a local bar to meet up with a few of my friends. One night, I noticed that there was no line outside. It was bitterly cold. There was a large, somewhere-in-his-thirties man standing outside, where the bouncer would usually be. I had been to this bar several times but had never encountered him. I walked up to him and assuming he was there to check IDs, I started digging in my purse for my wallet.

Before I knew it, he had me in a headlock and had started to drag me into a nearby alleyway. There was a whole bar full of people inside and this all played out literally just a few feet away from all of them. No one intervened. It's possible they didn't even see it (were the windows fogged up on this bitterly cold night? I can't remember).

Anyway, my sister asked me, "did you scream for help?"

Here's the thing — no, I didn't scream for help. Calling for help, yelling "HELP!" or "RAPE!" at the top of my lungs might seem the most "logical" thing to do, but I didn't say a word. I DO remember being hyper-focused on finding any part of his body that I could hurt, badly, so that he would release me from the headlock. I found an ear. With all my strength, I ripped down on that ear until it was hanging from his head by a thin piece of flesh. He let go.

More than twenty years later, in a conversation with my sister, she asked, "So, what happened next? Did you go inside the bar and meet up with your friends? Did you report it?"

And the truth is that I didn't. The details of what happened after that are ones I've re-constructed in my mind, to put the puzzle pieces together. How I got back to my dorm after the assault is lost to my memory — my understanding is a patchwork reconstruction of what probably happened based on a few things. The dorm was well within distance for a quick run. After he let go of me, my assailant probably staggered off into the night holding his bleeding face, and I probably ran home as fast as I could.

Here's what I learned from this experience. When one feels primally threatened, the hyper-focus on the source of the threat, and associated gaps in memory are a real thing.

In reflecting on my own experience, I appreciate the deeply vulnerable place that Michael was in. For whatever reason, we seem to assume that our police officers are not fully human — that even when their lives are threatened, they should be able to exercise perfect recall, in the ways they have been trained to observe and report. Add to this the fact that trial attorneys are skilled at identifying any inconsistencies in a person's story, which can lead us to doubt the credibility of a witness. During our prep for this chapter, Michael told me that when he realized he was not able to recall things clearly from the night of the shooting, he became "paranoid about not remembering" other important things.

In the context of the legal battle that ensued, this is not paranoia. Michael was fighting the darkness, and in the end, the darkness claimed his marriage.

ABOUT THE AUTHOR

Doc Shauna Springer

Relationship Expert.
Trauma Expert.
Trusted Doc.

Shauna "Doc" Springer is a best-selling author, frequently requested keynote speaker, and one of the world's leading experts on psychological trauma, military transition, suicide prevention, and close relationships. In addition to being the author of *WARRIOR: How to Support Those Who Protect Us*, she is the co-author of *BEYOND THE MILITARY: A Leader's Handbook for Warrior Reintegration.*

A Harvard graduate who has become a trusted Doc to our nation's military warfighters and first responders, she navigates diverse cultures with exceptional agility. As Chief Psychologist for Stella, she advances a new model for treating psychological trauma that combines biological and psychological interventions. Doc Springer is a licensed psychologist who is frequently sourced by the media for her uniquely perceptive insights on trauma recovery, post-traumatic growth, psychological health, and interpersonal relationships, developed from two decades of work at the extremes.

Doc Springer's work has been featured in multiple media outlets, including CNN, VICE, NPR, NBC, CBS Radio, *Forbes*, *Business Insider*, *Military Times*, Military.com, Gun Talk Radio, *Coffee or Die* Magazine, *Havok Journal*, THRIVE GLOBAL, *U.S. News and World Report*, *The Daily News*, RELIAS Media, Police1, Anxiety.org, *Washington Post*, and *Psychology Today*.

PEN FED Media Group filmed and produced a 2-minute video which captures the essence of Doc Springer's values and mission. You can view the video on youtube by searching: "PEN FED Doc Springer"

Doc Springer offers paid speaking, training, and strategic consultation. To make an inquiry, visit the "CONTACT" page on her website: https://www.docshaunaspringer.com/.

Follow Doc Shauna Springer's Work

www.linkedin.com/in/docshaunaspringer

https://twitter.com/Doc_Springer

https://www.instagram.com/docshaunaspringer/

Made in the USA
Las Vegas, NV
12 May 2021